GIVE ME LIBERTY

By HILDEGARDE HAWTHORNE

LONG ADVENTURE
The Story of Winston Churchill

PHANTOM KING:
The Story of Napoleon's Son

THE POET OF CRAIGIE HOUSE:
The Story of Henry Wadsworth Longfellow

ROMANTIC REBEL:
The Story of Nathaniel Hawthorne

GIVE ME LIBERTY

ISLAND FARM

TABITHA OF LONELY HOUSE

DEEDAH'S WONDERFUL YEAR

RIDERS OF THE ROYAL ROAD

THE MYSTERY OF STAR-C. RANCH

THE MYSTERY IN NAVAJO CANON

THE SECRET OF RANCHO DEL SOL

THE MINIATURE'S SECRET

MAKESHIFT FARM

The men had rushed to the cupola and torn down the flag.

GIVE ME LIBERTY

by

Hildegarde Hawthorne

Pictures by Woodi Ishmael

D. APPLETON-CENTURY COMPANY
Incorporated
NEW YORK   LONDON

Contents

vii

Illustrations

GIVE ME LIBERTY

Chapter 1

THREE WRONG TURNS TO THE RIGHT ROAD

THE Reverend Patrick Henry looked gravely at his brother John as the two sat together on the portico of the pleasant farmhouse, Mount Brilliant.

"You're too easy-going, John, as I've said before." The rector had driven over from the little rectory at Hanover town in his gig. "I've come to propose something I hope you'll agree to—no, wait till I explain, before you say anything. It has to do with your sons, as I've no doubt you guess.

"They are wasting their lives, as you know very well." He waved a dignified hand as John seemed about to utter a word. "William is close to seventeen, Patrick is fifteen. Neither are going to school, nor have done so since Pat-

the sport, the wonderful May afternoon, and the mere
fact of being alive. Tall for his age, thin, moving with an
easy, long stride, the boy looked older than his fifteen
years. His face was a long oval with a finely cut mouth
and firmly rounded chin. The forehead was high and
broad, the eyes striking, very long, rather deep-set and of
a brilliant blue, almost a flame under excitement or emotion. Between eyebrows that were slender and delicately
curved an aquiline nose lent a proud accent to the sensitive, intelligent ensemble, while the quick, slight smile,
both shy and amused, that came and went in an instant,
was the friendliest thing imaginable.

Deciding he had fish enough, Patrick sat down under a
beech tree, pulled a flute out of a pocket, and leaning back
against the smooth trunk, began tootling a gay little tune,
presently yanking off his hat to let the cool breeze
blow through his red hair, tied in a short queue. A mock-
ing bird flew to a bough over him and began singing,
even trying an imitative trill or two. Pat laughed,
stretched himself, lifting his arms high and wide, gazing
upward.

"Reckon I'd best be going back home," he announced,
to the attentive bird. "Ho-hum! Wish I had a pair of wings,
too." He rose slowly, thinking. Uncle Patrick was coming
to supper, and he felt fairly certain, from some scattered
remarks, that Uncle was coming with a purpose, a purpose
involving himself. The thought both alarmed and interested him. Uncle Patrick was a forceful, high-tempered,
generous man. Without these characteristics he could not
have done for St. Paul's parish what he had done. From a
disintegrated, careless, and worldly set of parishioners he
had created a devoted following who came to his church
because of his preaching, because of his leadership, because

he had refused to permit the house of God to fulfil merely
a social demand, as was all too much the case in the Established Church of that day in Virginia. Young Patrick both
loved and admired him, but he could not help that alarm
when he guessed that his uncle was turning his attention
toward his nephews.

The boy shoved his flute back into his pocket, jammed
his hat on, and tramped back to the house.

"But I won't let him make a clergyman of me," Pat declared aloud, swinging his creel over his shoulder.

Behind Patrick stretched a long line of professional men,
ministers of the Gospel predominating. The Henrys had
come from Normandy with William the Conqueror in
1066, several brothers and brothers' sons of them, to scat-
ter over the new country, some in England, one branch in
Ireland, others in Scotland; and it was these latter who
helped build Aberdeen, the "Silver City," from whom this
American branch had descended. The city's lovely nickname was given because, as their father told the boys, it
was all built of a glimmering type of granite, clear and
smooth, that after rain glistened like silver. Father was
proud of his race:

"Yes, Patrick, we've been in the British story ever since
it began. Our name's in the *Livre des Conquérants,* the
Roll of Battle Abbey, in *Domesday Book,* and half a century later, 1153, in the *Great Rolls of the Pipe,* for Scotland. Soldiers first, of course, and later good sound citizens,
farmers, doctors, lawyers, ministers of the Episcopal
Church—when England broke with the Catholics, and
some of us Highlanders went with them."

Sarah Winston Henry, the mother of the Henry children, came of a Yorkshire family that was also connected
with history, and claimed cousinship with John Churchill,

first Duke of Marlborough, son of Winston Churchill,
Master of the Horse under Charles I, ancestor of to-day's
great British statesman. The Virginian Winstons had come
to the colony at the beginning of the Eighteenth Century,
too late to acquire one of the great tidewater plantations,
but not too late to find excellent farmlands. Sarah was a
young widow when John Henry, fresh from Scotland, met
her, living with her only child on the estate her husband,
Colonel John Syme (Sim, he pronounced it), had given
her, Studley Manor. The two married a year or two later,
and about the time Patrick was born, May 29, 1736, moved
to Mount Brilliant, as healthier for growing children. His
Uncle Patrick had followed his brother from Aberdeen
about the time John had married, and through his wife's
connections John had been able to get him a parish.

It all made a good, exciting family story, young Patrick
was thinking, as he walked homeward brooding both over
the past and the future. His half brother, John Syme, was
already established at Studley Manor, managing it for his
mother until, at her death, it would come to him. He was
married to a pretty young wife and doing well. But, mused
Patrick, how about brother William and himself? What
would they do? William, Bill as the family called him,
planned to have a farm of his own one of these days, and
to breed fine horses. As to himself, however, he had no
definite notion. He was very happy at home in the big,
cheerful family, he adored his six sisters who would soon
be seven, and no one ever had a mother more serene of
spirit, with a laughing gentleness that, his father insisted,
made her the most charming woman in the world. It kept
her young, too, in spite of all her children. Yet Patrick
knew his father was troubled as to the future. Mount Brilliant paid for itself, but without much to spare.

Patrick really walked out of his boyhood on that evening in May, just before his fifteenth birthday.

For it was a strangely different life on which Patrick entered a week later. Long hours, but he did not find them tedious. It was interesting looking out at the world from the inside of the big shop. Up to now Patrick's contacts there had been short; errands for the family, usually with his father, sometimes with his mother, a little chat with a neighbor's son. Now he was part of the place, helping the farmers who came with their produce to swap for needed merchandise, and who usually had plenty to say for themselves, not only concerning local affairs, but politics. There were lively arguments, helped at times by some member of the House of the Burgesses, by a big planter, or the manager of a plantation. All sorts of men, all sorts of ideas. Pat enjoyed it. Enjoyed, too, talking of what he'd heard to the family.

"How do you like mixing with the world?" His father smiled at him.

"I like it. And it's curious what different ideas men can have on the same thing. I don't mean as between a clever and a stupid man, either. Just different judgments. You learn a lot hearing two or three sides of the same question."

He threw back his head in a characteristic gesture:

"You know, Father, I like that—seeing all around a thing. Sometimes I feel I'd like—" He paused.

"Well, my son?"

"To be a lawyer myself."

The year swept by and with the following June William and Patrick found themselves established in the small general store which Uncle Patrick had helped the boys' father to stock. These stores carried a vast variety of merchandise, seeking to provide everything likely to be called for by either town or country folk. Tobacco, or tobacco certificates issued by the public storehouses along the coast, was the chief means of exchange, for currency was scarce— a little of it English, more, Spanish silver coming from Florida. Swapping produce for necessities was another general practice. The Colony was not permitted to coin her own currency, and she was severely restricted as to home manufactures. More, all the tobacco she raised had to be sold to England, except the amount needed for her own consumption. It had its fixed rate, established by the Assembly and ratified by the king. This had originally been eight shillings and fourpence the hundred pounds; fifty years later, in 1748, the price was raised fifty per cent. All business transactions, salaries, expenses of all sorts, were paid in tobacco at this rate. The only exception was the salary paid each of the clergy. That had been set at sixteen thousand pounds of leaf at the earlier rate and remained the same after its increase in value. For the tobacco England returned not specie, but everything the colony needed which she neither raised nor made herself.

This involved transaction worked out fairly well so long as affairs remained stable. Unluckily for the new shop, however, the French were beginning to trouble the border, claiming the land along the Ohio, which Virginia considered her own. This threat, constantly increasing, and ending in the French Border War in 1754 that dragged along until 1760, played havoc with a small enterprise like the Henry brothers' shop. Especially as they didn't know how to refuse credit. The little place was well supplied and attractive, and Patrick at least worked hard; but early in 1753, before it was a year old, the enterprise blew up. William departed, leaving Pat to settle the business as well as he could, which took the greater part of the year. In the end he recovered most of what was owing, squared what he owed, and came through with a small surplus.

Patrick was all of eighteen by this time. In between settling with his creditors he had kept his spirits up by deer hunting and by falling in love. The fair one was a year younger than himself, Sarah, daughter of one of the shop's customers, Mr. John Shelton, a farmer at The Forks, where the North and South Anna joined. Miss Shelton was by all accounts a cheerful, pretty girl. Now that he was in the clear Patrick proposed, was accepted, and in the autumn of 1754 the two youngsters were married. Sarah's dowry was a piece of land known as Pine Slash, fifteen slaves, several of them children, and her parents' blessing. Patrick's father presented the couple with an adjoining tract of land and five grown Negroes. There was a small house on Pine Slash, and here the two set up housekeeping. Patrick was now a farmer. Both fathers added gifts of pigs, sheep, a work horse, a plow, and other such necessities, as well as furniture for the home.

It was hard work, but it was fun and the two were happy.

When the first year was over they were three, the newcomer a girl, named Martha. The land proved none too good, and one day Patrick, coming back from the swim he always took after work, remarked that they were getting by, "but this is not the life I mean to live forever." Patrick was speaking from the bedroom where he was putting on fresh linen. He was very finicky always about his underclothing and stockings, though coat and breeches might look dusty and shabby. Sarah laughed:

"But, Pat, you'll soon have a son helping you on the farm." For it was late in 1756 and Sally was "expecting."

"We'll be driving in a coach of our own by the time he's fit to help me, Sally. Won't we look fine?"

"We'll wear nothing but silks and velvets, and you'll have a powdered wig and lace ruffles at your wrists and throat," Sally returned, giving her husband a smile as he came out on the portico, looking fresh and tidy, his hair in a tight queue. Pat reached for the little girl on her lap, tossed her high, and returned her squeaking with delight to her mother.

"Certainly. And the little chap and Patsy [his nickname for Martha] will look like a prince and princess."

Sure enough, with the year's end, a son, John, was born.

The Future may have grinned at the two, who little dreamed how much of this amused boasting would come true.

However, late next year, 1757, Pine Slash burned to the ground. Only a few pieces of furniture were saved, but no one was harmed. Patrick was twenty-one, Virginia Colony a hundred and fifty years old.

"Nice celebration for my coming of age," he remarked, as he and Sally watched the flames, his arm around her shoulders. "I suppose one of the Negroes started it by some carelessness. We'll say nothing. It's done. You're a fine girl!" For Sally neither whimpered nor grieved.

She and the children went to Mount Brilliant. Selling three of his slaves Pat raised enough money to start a small store, hiring a clerk to attend to it, while he gave most of his own time to the farm. As luck had it, the French border war was now at full tilt, and not alone that, but the 1758 tobacco crop was a dire failure. This was serious. Even the rich suffered the following year, and the poor hardly knew where to turn. Fortunately the farm did well, there was plenty of food and Patrick was able to help his father feed

"Nice celebration for my coming of age!"

the family. As for his customers, they dwindled to nothing.

That Christmas of 1759-60 young Henry and his wife were asked to spend the holidays at the Dandridges. Sally was expecting another child but she insisted on Pat's going. He needed a rest and change, and the Dandridges were good friends of his family, for their estate was only a few miles from Mount Brilliant; Captain Dandridge was devoted to Pat's father, with whom he delighted to play chess and talk over British history. The Captain was a retired navy officer, a fine man with a charming wife, several pretty daughters, still children, and plenty of money.

Patrick was already certain that both his farm and his shop were headed for failure. He was not sorry. Neither farming nor running a store was to his mind work to which he could devote a lifetime. The vague thought of becoming a lawyer had remained in his mind. He knew a great many people, some of importance. He had spent a considerable amount of time, when he and William were attempting to make a go of the store near Hanover Court House, attending cases being tried, and had found them interesting. Especially the examination of a witness fascinated him. This drawing out of a man's thoughts, these revelations of human nature struck him as worth while. Snatching the truth from a tangle of lies; swinging opinions in the way you desired them to flow. Yes, he'd like that kind of work. He might say something to the Captain, get his opinion.

It was during this visit that Henry and Thomas Jefferson met each other for the first time. Their lives, through the events waiting ahead, were to run fairly close together. Jefferson would be seventeen the coming April, Patrick, twenty-four. From an early liking and admiration Jefferson was to develop a jealousy amounting to hatred, that led him, after Henry's death, when he was asked for details respecting the past by Henry's first biographer, William Wirt, to supply much that was not only unfair but untrue. So it is interesting to read what Jefferson has to say more than thirty years later, about this first meeting.

After mentioning that both were guests of the Dandridges he continues:

"During the festivities of the season I met him every day and we became well acquainted, although I was much his junior ... His manners had something of coarseness, [in those days the word was used to express *countrified*] his passion was music, dancing, and pleasantry. He excelled in the last, and it attached every one to him. You ask some account of his mind and information at this period, but you will recollect that we were almost continually engaged in the revelries of the season. The occasion perhaps, as much as his idle disposition, prevented his engaging in any conversation that might give the measure either of his mind or information. Opportunity was not, indeed, wholly lacking, because Mr. John Campbell was there, who had married Mrs. Spottswood, the sister of Colonel [the Captain must have been the only Colonel in the British Navy!] Dandridge. He was a man of science and often introduced science into the conversation. Mr. Henry had, a little before, broken up his store—or rather, it had broken him up; but his misfortune was not traced, either in his countenance or conduct."

No, Henry wasn't given to weeping on other people's shoulders, nor had he come to a Christmas party for any purpose but to enjoy himself with good friends he'd known for years. Certainly he would not confide in a boy on his way to matriculate at William and Mary College, totally unknown to him, nor discuss with a scientist a science of which he probably knew nothing. Moreover, at this season, the store had neither been broken nor broken him. It was sold seven months later with what goods it still had, to a single firm at a fair price. Patrick had debts, but they were paid in full, and he was able to say, at the end of his life, that he had never been sued.

Young Henry had great talents, as yet unproved, even unguessed. But they made him strong. Life, he believed, was a fit adversary, a noble one, even at moments, when it thought it had you down, an amusing one. He never wanted, as he wrote years later to a young friend, "uninterrupted tranquillity," insisting that "adversity toughens a man," and that it is far better to "surmount the evils of life than to be exempted from them."

In the spring following the Dandridges' party Patrick strode swiftly, amazingly forward on the path that was to be his. Behind him lay three failures, but they were not wasted; they combined to teach him life and train him for success. No more wasted than those forest wanderings that delighted what Jefferson called his "idle disposition."

Even so would Lincoln, years later, be sneered at by the school and college bred as a raw ignoramus. People are rarely funnier than when they express their notions as to what does, or does not, make an educated man. They forget that it is not how you come through, but what you come through with, that is the essential.

Chapter 2

AND NOW, FOR THE LAW!

NOT very long after the Christmas holidays Patrick became convinced that there wasn't a chance of making a living out of shop and farm. Things grew worse unremittedly. Unless he was ready to accept charity or to starve with his wife and children, it was time to leave the path along which he'd been scrambling and sliding since the age of sixteen, and find another road.

"I've decided on trying for the law, Sally," he told his wife. "I've been thinking of it for quite some time, and I'm fairly certain I've got an understanding of men and some aptitude for legal argument. I've listened often enough at the Court House to other men to know what's required to win your case. I've been talking to

Attorney Lewis and he agrees with me that I've a gift for debate. All that's needed is to learn enough to apply for a licence. I don't think that will take very long."

Sally was the sort of woman who believed in her husband, in spite of the rough road the two had had to travel. Why shouldn't he make a lawyer? She knew several young men who were making their living as lawyers, and she knew that Patrick was quite as clever as they. It seemed an excellent idea to her, and she told him so.

The following day Patrick borrowed two books from Mr. Lewis, *Coke upon Littleton* and a *Digest of the Virginia Acts.*

For the next six weeks he ate, slept, and read law. Most of each of the twenty-four hours were given to Coke. With the amazing gift for application which, with his equally amazing memory and his clear understanding of the essentials of any given problem, were the working elements of his genius, he then felt he had mastered enough law to pass the necessary examination.

His friend Mr. Lewis was considerably surprised to have young Henry come in to say he thought he was ready to try for his license.

"Good heavens, Patrick, don't tell me you've finished with Coke! Not to mention the Virginia Acts?"

"No, I won't say I've finished with Coke, but I've got enough of him to do, I believe, and the Acts I have pretty well by heart—try me out a little, if you'll be so good."

So the lawyer tried him out, skipping from one section to another. At the end of a half-hour he closed the books and studied his young friend with a long, considering look.

"I've never known the law to be taken by storm until this morning, Patrick. But you've done it. Of course, you'll need to study it far more completely, but I believe you will be given your license. Williamsburg is the place and I advise you to ride there at once and try your luck. And my blessing goes along with you."

So, in the early spring, off rode young Henry, in his somewhat shabby country suit. His horse was a farm horse, his hat had no style, he wore no ruffles. He was a poor man and made no bones about it. He had come to the capital to see the men who could admit him to the profession at which, he believed, he would earn a decent income, and he had come for no other reason than to have at it. He looked what he was, tall, thin, eager, hopeful, country bred and country dressed. John Lewis had told him where to make his application to appear before the Board of Examiners, and given him the name of a small inn where he could put up.

It is generally agreed that the four men on the Board to whom Henry particularly applied were George Wythe, Peyton and John Randolph, and Robert Carter Nicholas. There were none more distinguished in their profession.

Wythe, after hearing how short a time Henry had been reading law, refused to pass him, and seems not to have made the least attempt to discover how fit the young applicant might be in spite of that fact. Each of the examiners saw him separately. Mr. Nicholas talked with him for some time, as did the third man, Peyton Randolph. Both signed the application. The last, John Randolph, who later became the last royal Attorney-General for the Colony, at first showed very little interest in examining the shabby young applicant, and it was only when he heard that his elder brother and Mr. Nicholas had signed, that he, too, agreed to examine him.

These two Randolphs were the sons of Sir John Randolph, who had come from England, with a grant of land

and the knighthood bestowed by his king, to develop one of the great tidewater estates and tobacco plantations. He had died in 1737, when Peyton was seventeen. It was this family with which, through his mother, Jefferson was connected. John Randolph was a dyed-in-the-wool Tory, a man of elegance, tall and handsome, with grave and stately manners. Patrick afterwards told a friend, John Tyler, later a judge, of this interview, and he, in time to come, told Wirt.

Henry was quick to see that Mr. Randolph totally disapproved of his appearance and expected the worst. Whether or not he had read Alexander Pope's dictum, "The proper study of mankind is man," Patrick, as we know, had adopted it with enthusiasm. But after a few questions to which Henry replied with what Mr. Tyler calls "the peculiar texture and strength of his style and the boldness and originality of his combinations," the examiner began to get interested.

"I could see he was surprised," Henry told his friend, "and presently he began to play off on me the sort of tactics I've used when I'm trying to draw out some man in the shop, get at what he really knows and feels and how he thinks. The examination took several hours and to me, at least, was tremendously interesting. After a few questions on municipal law he knew that he could never pass me on that. I'd given it little attention, to tell you the truth. So he turned to query me about the laws of nature, of nations, on the policy of the feudal system, and not only that, but on history in general. I'm rather strong in that and talk of it easily, and, I think, widely. Presently he swung off to the common law, and when I replied to one of his questions, he dissented sharply, calling on me to give the reasons for my opinion. This brought on an argument, and he began drawing me out, trying to confuse me with subtleties, or to dash me with a burst of eloquence, and I could feel that he was watching each defensive operation of my brain. I enjoyed it. After considerable discussion he said, 'You defend your opinion well, Sir, but now to the law and the testimony,' carrying me off to his office, where, opening the authorities, he looked gravely at me for a moment, saying: 'Behold the force of natural reasoning; you have never seen these books, nor this principle of the law; yet you are right and I am wrong, and, from this lesson you've given me, and you must excuse me for saying it, I will never trust to appearances again. Mr. Henry; if your industry be only half equal to your genius, I augur you will do well, and become an ornament and honor to your profession.' And so, Tyler, I was passed. I knew very well when he opened the books and gave me that glance, that he had taken the wrong side to test me. And I can tell you, Tyler, that I rode away from Williamsburg with my heart singing, jubilant."

And now for another glance at that letter by Jefferson, written in 1814 in reply to William Wirt, who was seeking biographical material. He and Patrick met somewhere, probably on the college grounds, and, Jefferson tells us, Henry "told me he had been reading law only six weeks." But, he goes on, "two of the examiners, Peyton and John Randolph, men of great facility of temper, signed his license with as much reluctance as their dispositions would permit them to show. Mr. Wythe absolutely refused. Robert C. Nicholas refused also at first, but on repeated importunity and promise of future reading, he signed. These facts I had afterwards from the gentlemen themselves, the two Randolphs acknowledging he was very ignorant of the law, but that they perceived him to be a young man of genius, and did not doubt he would soon qualify himself."

Ten years later, speaking to Daniel Webster at Monticello, Webster having come to get information on Virginian leaders in the Revolution, Jefferson, who had but two more years to live, in this instance had dropped Nicholas and put Edmund Pendleton in his place, but he had lost none of his rancor. He says:

There were four examiners, Wythe, Pendleton, Peyton Randolph and John Randolph. Wythe and Pendleton at once rejected his application; the two Randolphs were, by his importunity, prevailed upon to sign the license; and having obtained their signatures, he again applied to Pendleton, and after much entreaty and many promises of future study, succeeded also in obtaining his. He then turned out for a practicing lawyer.

How, one wonders, did a freshman of barely seventeen get all this information! Did these learned men rush to give it him, and why? And if Jefferson was unable to remember which of two men had been among the examiners, how could he so clearly remember the rest of his information? It would not matter except that other such bitter and careless statements in regard to Patrick Henry, given to men who were to publish what he said, are chalked up against Jefferson, as we shall see.

Having got back home and reported the good news to his family and friends, Henry sat down to reading more law before beginning to practice, in the latter half of September. His mother's brother, the second Isaac Winston, had married a Fontaine, daughter of one of the leading Huguenot families of the Colony, whose brother gave Patrick a copy of *Forms of Declaration and Pleas,* an invaluable volume for a young attorney. On the flyleaf, in

Henry's writing is inscribed: "Le don de Pierre de la Fontaine" and the signature, "Patrice Henry le Jeune, son livre, Avrille 18, 1760." Patrick had an odd way of occasionally using junior after his name, as though the man he'd been named for were his father instead of his uncle. Henry, despite the wrong spelling, had quite a smattering of French, probably acquired by more or less intercourse with these French connections of his family.

Henry's fee books, carefully kept and beginning in September, 1760, on the page following the last entry in regard to his store, are convincing evidence of the immediate success he achieved.

On September 19th Patrick entered the final item regarding his store, a matter of twenty-five pounds received from the firm of Grenshaw and Grant for the remaining goods in his possession. Then he began the index of his fees. These were charged by the year. This first page, together with fifteen others scattered through the record, which extended to the end of 1763, had been cut out by autograph hunters before the family put the folio out of reach. However, the entries for the few months which remain show that in this first year of his practice Patrick was able to list the names of sixty clients, the first being a firm of merchants, Coutts & Crosse.

This remarkably good record is a clear sign of young Henry's personal popularity among his neighbors, as of their confidence both in his ability and his willingness to work. The books are kept with careful neatness in his own handwriting, and show that the clients he made remained with him, and that new ones were constantly added. During those last months of 1760 he charged one hundred and seventy-five fees. By the end of '63 he had charged fees for one thousand, one hundred and eighty-five suits, besides a large number for legal advice and for preparing papers out of court. He was indeed kept steadily at work with all the varying business of a country practice, his field extending through the county courts of Hanover and the counties surrounding. These county courts, throughout Virginia, were the only ones in the Colony, except for the General Court at Williamstown, presided over by the Governor and the Council.

No better training for a young attorney than these courts, which gave opportunity to become familiar with every branch of his profession, existed. Henry could never have acquired, still less retained his knowledge, without faithful and attentive work. Much of it was more or less dull routine, and a man had to be both devoted and eager to make a success so marked.

It proved fortunate that these careful records were kept. They show he charged the moderate fees regulated by law, many for drawing papers, many where he was the only counsel, together with more important work, and that he was by no means rigid in collecting his fees, often permitting them to run over the very liberal time he gave. Fortunate indeed that they survive, if for no other reason than to disprove Jefferson's statements written to Wirt when Henry was safe in his grave. Here is a sample:

He turned his views to the law, for the acquisition or practice of which he was too lazy... He never undertook to draw pleadings if he could avoid it, or to manage that part of the cause, and very unwillingly engaged but as an assistant to speak in the cause, and the fee was an indispensable preliminary, observing to the applicant that he kept no accounts, never putting them to paper, which was true.

It was not true, as the books, which Thomas Jefferson did not know existed, easily prove. They also prove that

Henry's success as a lawyer was far beyond Mr. Jefferson's.

Henry was not only able to pay off any remaining debts, but also to assist his own father and Mr. Skelton, his father-in-law, both of whom were having a struggle to make both ends meet. Skelton had opened a tavern near Hanover Court House, where Patrick stayed when attending that court. Jefferson seized upon this fact to tell Wirt: "He acted, as I have understood, as a barkeeper in the tavern at Hanover Court House for some time." Wirt evidently doubted this, for he went to see Colonel Samuel Meredith, who had known Henry for the whole of his life, and also to Dr. Moses Coit Tyler, who was a longtime friend. Both were furious at the charge, Tyler taking great pains, with Wirt, to sift the matter thoroughly, and the two men going on record as satisfied that there was no truth whatever in Jefferson's slur. Nor was there in another Jefferson was fond of making—after Henry's death, be it noted, and to strangers who had never seen or heard him—that Henry's pronunciation was "vicious and vulgar." Henry was a good mimic, and in telling a story, or making a point in a law case, he could and did copy country and uneducated pronunciation, and he probably used country idioms, as did men like Edmund Pendleton, who used to say "scaicely," for scarcely, though he was among the top-shelf elegants of Williamsburg. Truth is Jefferson never forgave Henry for being a better lawyer, for having a strong, flexible, and dramatic voice, while his own was poor and feeble, nor yet for Henry's success as Governor of Virginia, an office in which Jefferson himself dismally failed. Yet, in his more generous youth, he had listened to Henry speak with spellbound enthusiasm.

After all, Henry came from a learned family, he was kin to several of the fine colonial families, his father was now a

presiding judge of Hanover County, he himself was on the
point of appearing in a famous cause and to make an un-
forgettable speech in the fluent and beautiful English with
which he was able to charm men's minds and move their
hearts. Jefferson's charges were absurd, the mean revenge
of an old man brooding over past irritations, but coming
from him they harmed Henry's memory to some extent.
It is time that they were exposed and forgotten, and that
a popular notion that Henry was lazy, uneducated, and
that he acquired his fame by having the luck to make a
few great speeches at periods of crisis, was blotted out. It
simply is not true.

Chapter 3

HENRY STEPS INTO THE LIMELIGHT

IN 1755 a serious drought practically ruined the tobacco crop all over Virginia. Since tobacco was the money of the Colony it played the deuce with the financial situation. The price of the little that was harvested soared—very much as though the leaves had been paper money thrown into a great fire, with paper money the only currency, thus forcing the few remaining bills far up beyond their printed value.

To meet the situation the Assembly passed an Act making all bills payable in cash or in promissory notes rated at the staple price of tobacco, twopence a pound, to hold for ten months, when the new crop would become available. The people still suffered somewhat, but on the whole the scheme worked well. Every one accepted it, even when it involved a sacrifice. Every one, that is, but a proportion of the clergy, who insisted on their pound of flesh, in this case sixteen thousand pounds of tobacco, no matter how high it rose. That was the law, and that was that.

But enough ministers remained who felt it was not right for the Church to profit at the expense of the populace, and in a convention called by them, this was agreed to, and the matter concluded. With the next year the situation returned to normal.

Then, in 1758, it became clear that the crop would again be scanty, and the Assembly revived the Tuppenny Act, as it was popularly known. Once again every one accepted its consequences, whether in salaries, for debts, or trade as usual. Once again, too, the clergy protested. One among them, the Reverend John Camm, published a furious article in the *Gazette*, bitterly assailing the Assembly. He was as bitterly answered in the same paper by Colonels Richard Bland and Landon Carter, men of the highest standing. Almost to a man the colonists sided against Mr. Camm, and the *Gazette* refused to publish a second article by that gentleman, who was forced to get it printed in Maryland as a small pamphlet, entitled *The Colonels Dismounted,* which made some of Virginia laugh and all of it angry. Thereupon the clergy called a convention which made Mr. Camm its envoy to London with a Petition to the King. By now the Parsons' Cause, as it came to be called, was the only thing talked about in the Colony.

Mr. Camm had a high card up his sleeve—the clause in the Colonial law that made no Act legal passed by the Assembly, even with the Governor's signature, unless it received the King's approval. It was a bad clause, since the

King knew little or nothing of Colonial affairs, and it was indeed usually dispensed with, since it took many weeks to go and return from England with the necessary papers. The Tuppenny Act had never made the trip and consequently was not strictly legal.

Mr. Camm returned in triumph. The King, God bless him, had disallowed the Act, which made it illegal from its inception. All this had taken time. It was autumn, 1759, before Camm could bring a suit in the General Court, Williamsburg, to test the law.

"If I fail there," he promised, "I'll appeal to the King in Council."

The Assembly retorted that it would stand the expenses of all appeals brought against the clergy. Several ministers, scattered about the Colony, brought suits in various Court Houses, but, with, to the layman, the inexplicable delays of the law, the first to be acted upon was brought by the Reverend Mr. Maury in Hanover County Court House, in 1762. His counsel was Mr. Peter Lyons, the most distinguished lawyer in that part of the Colony. Opposing him, as counsel for the defendants, was John Lewis, the able lawyer who had counselled Patrick Henry to apply for a license to practice. This first meeting was merely a gesture. Mr. Lewis cited the Act passed by the Assembly, with which his clients had strictly complied, and Mr. Lyon entered a demurrer that this plea was insufficient, thus raising the question of the validity of the Act.

Then every one returned to the usual occupations of life until November, 1763.

At this date Patrick's father was the presiding judge, and he and the associate judges had but one point to settle. What was the law in this case? It was clear. They had to sustain the demurrer, which meant that the Act by the Assembly was null and void, and had been so from its initiation. It took courage with the state of public opinion, not to mention their own sympathies, but they were there to judge the law itself, not whether it was a good or a bad law, but whether it existed. Their decision settled the law of the case, and but one further step was required—a trial by jury, to settle what amount of damages was due the plaintiff. Mr. Lewis looked upon his case as lost, and withdrew. It would be tried on December 1st.

Very naturally Patrick Henry had followed the case intently, with all that led up to it. He agreed with his father that he had rendered the only decision possible. For some years now John Henry had been a judge in Hanover, and a good one. But Pat did not agree that such a law was right nor that it ought to be permitted. It was tyranny, he declared, and tyranny should be fought. The Act passed by the Assembly had been a good Act, honest and necessary. No distant monarch had a right to destroy it.

There had been plenty of talk throughout the neigborhood, and Henry's opinion was known. It was also known that he was an excellent lawyer, and especially successful with juries. Why not ask him to step into the place left vacant by Mr. Lewis? So a small deputation waited on him.

"Will you fight for us, Mr. Henry?"

He looked at the men, and his heart beat high. All his love for liberty, for the rights of the people, clamored in him. Here was a bad law, bolstered by an absurd custom. Virginia must make her own laws some day. Why not begin now to break this tyranny of an absent king? You got nowhere without trying, without daring.

"Yes, gentlemen, I'll fight for this cause, the people's cause, against the Parsons' Cause. With all I have in me!"

December 1st proved a chill, damp, gloomy day. But from early morning the crowd began to gather and the moment the doors of the Court House opened the room began to fill. On a platform at one end of the large hall was the presiding judge's chair, with a long bench on either side for the assisting judges, and back of these another long bench for the clergy. Besides these were the witness stand, the jury box, the bar separating all from the audience, which, since no benches were provided, had to stand, jammed together from wall to wall.

Patrick waited outside on the porch, under one of the five fine arches that extended across the entire front of the handsome little building. He was watching for some one.

A carriage containing his Reverend Uncle Patrick drove up. At once the young man approached it:

"Uncle, will you do me a great favor?"

"Assuredly, my boy. What is it?"

"Not to appear in the Court House this morning."

"Bless my soul, why not?"

"Because, Sir, as you know, I am here in opposition to the clergy—and your appearance in court will strike me with such awe I could not do my clients justice."

"Well, well! Rather than that should happen, I'll not only keep out of the Court but I'll go back home." And off he was driven by his black coachman.

Brother-in-law Samuel Meredith appeared at the instant, and winked at Pat.

"It's bad enough, Sam, to have my father presiding, without Uncle Patrick sitting with the rest of the clergy, looking on at my struggles. Come, let's go inside."

Peter Lyons, appearing for Mr. Maury, had, like Patrick, been born at Studley Manor. A few years later the estate had been sold to Mr. Syme, who brought to it his bride,

Patrick's mother-to-be, as we know. Lyons had known Patrick since he was a baby, and always called him "young Pat." He was to feel young Pat's mettle to-day.

The jury chosen, the preliminaries over, Mr. Lyons rose and opened his argument for the plaintiff. It amounted to the clear statement that the issue had been narrowed, by the decision of the court on the law, to the difference between the sum paid the plaintiff, one hundred and forty-four pounds, and the value of sixteen thousand pounds of tobacco at fifty shillings a pound.

Possibly sensing that this sounded rather raw, he launched into an eloquent rush of praise for the noble spirit of benevolence that had always characterized the clergy, and sat down. No one laughed, but there were some who grinned.

It was Patrick's turn.

He rose rather slowly, faced the jury, but seemed unable to begin speaking. At last he stammered a sentence or two, looking to be almost in agony. The people stared at him, horrified. Some hung their heads in bitter disappointment, while the clergy exchanged glances of triumph. As for his father, the Judge, he sank lower and lower in his chair, gazing at the floor.

Suddenly Henry straightened, lifted his head, sent a flashing look about the room. Why should he be troubled about this august court, about these learned and distinguished ministers? He stood there for something greater —for the people—and he stood alone. The people, whose livelihood was to be snatched from them, and whose freedom to make the laws under which they must live and work was to be denied them.

He made a gesture full of grace and dignity, that seemed to sweep away all fear, all opposition. He began to speak, in a voice gentle, yet reaching, of the issues that had brought them here together.

"Government," he said, "is a conditional compact, depending on mutual and dependable covenants. The King gives his people protection, the people return him their obedience and support. But if this covenant is broken by either party, it releases the other from obligation."

In swift sentences he likened the colonial government to the government of England. The House of Burgesses stood for the House of Commons, the Council for the House of Lords, the Governor for the King. Each had responsibilities and duties. And any law approved by these three must stand until they disallowed it. Briefly he surveyed the Acts of 1755-58 and the necessity that brought them into being, creating and maintaining a law—"a law," he declared, "that has every characteristic of a good law. It is a law of general utility, and consistent with the compact between King and People, it cannot be annulled against the wish of the People."

He paused, looking about him gravely, and now his voice took on a note of authority, even of menace: "The King has seen fit to disallow this salutary Act. Here is an instance of misrule, of a complete neglect for the welfare of this Colony. The King, from being the father of his people," and his voice rang out, "has become a tyrant, forfeiting all right to his subjects' obedience, and making it necessary for the people, to insure their future safety, to adhere to this their Act—" At this point Mr. Lyons cried angrily: "The gentleman is speaking treason!" and from the benches where the ministers sat came a confused mutter of "Treason, treason," and Lyons again called out, "I am astonished that your Worships can listen to him without emotion or any mark of dissatisfaction." It was not the last time Henry would have that word, treason, hurled at him. Now he took no notice of it, but swept on with his denunciation while the judges sat spellbound, and some of the jury nodded their heads in assent to what he was saying. As for the audience, the people all stood motionless, staring at Henry, their eyes flashing back at his, while, as one among them put it afterwards, "he made our blood run cold and our hair to stand on end."

Swinging from King to the clergy Patrick declared that beyond their religious duties, their social responsibility was to enforce by their own behaviour respect for civil laws and responsibilities. "Yet is it not true that the clergy of Virginia, in this particular instance of refusal to accept the law enacted here for the benefit of the entire Colony, have failed to carry out one of the great ends of their institution? Instead of acting as useful members of the State, they have behaved as enemies to the community. In this case now before the gentlemen of the jury, Mr. Maury, instead of countenance and protection and damages, justly deserves to be punished with severity.

"We have heard a great deal about the benevolence and holy zeal of our reverend clergy, but how is it manifested? Do they prove their zeal by practicing the mild and beneficent precepts of Jesus? Do they feed the hungry and clothe the naked? Oh no, gentlemen! Instead of feeding the hungry and clothing the naked these rapacious harpies would, were their powers equal to their will, snatch from the hearth of their honest parishioner his last hoecake, from the widow and her orphan children their last milch-cow, and the bed, nay, the last blanket, from the lying-in woman!"

Patrick had spoken with a burning scorn. His gestures seemed to create the scene back of his words, and the people, silent and tense, forgot everything but Henry, speaking, compelling, holding them motionless and still under the passion of his words, of his whole being. They felt that genius had suddenly flowered before them, that a man had come to his own, and that his own was greatness.

Though there was no sound the feeling he roused in his audience became like a wave of anger and contempt that pressed against the ministers. They got to their feet, hurriedly, confusedly, to leave not alone the courtroom, but the building.

But Henry was not yet content to end. He went on to describe the bondage of a people not permitted to make their own laws, telling the jury that, unless they wished to rivet the chains on their necks, they must refuse to let the opportunity now presented slip by. They must make an example of the plaintiff, an example that should warn him and all his brethren not again to dispute the validity of laws such as this, made for the people by the representatives and leaders of the people, the only authority—Burgesses, Council, and understanding Governor—which, to his mind, could give force to the law.

Then, with a sudden, smiling relaxation, a slight shrug of the shoulders, he concluded:

"Of course, gentlemen, under the ruling of the Court, you, the Jury, must find for the plaintiff. But you need not find more than one farthing—which will accomplish all the defense desires."

Henry's talk had lasted close upon an hour. Mr. Lyons, in a few words, closed the case for his client, trying, although he knew it to be in vain, to break the spell Henry's words had thrown over all in the courtroom. The jury went out. Five restless minutes passed, they returned. The verdict was one penny damages for the plaintiff. Mr. Lyons entered an objection, demanding the jury be sent out to reconsider, claiming the verdict was contrary to the evidence. He was overruled by the Court, he moved for a new trial, was refused. Then he demanded an appeal to the General Court, which was granted.

The audience had been stirring and muttering through these formalities. And now, as Court adjourned, the crowd rushed in, Henry was swung up on the shoulders of two tall men, and marched out through the doorway, amid a roar of cheers and shouts, to circle the courtyard. Hands reached up to snatch his, voices called a word of thanks or praise, until finally he was set down at the doorway and permitted to return to the group within.

Patrick's father had sat watching his son through this amazing metamorphosis with tears of joy and pride filling his eyes. The two now clasped hands in silence. It was not only the fact that Patrick had proved himself a great orator, but also that he had shown absolute fearlessness in attacking, thus openly and powerfully, the tyranny of Church and State, which Virginia had long felt, that moved his father. With true Scottish restraint Mr. John Henry, speaking to one of his friends who dropped in later at his home to offer congratulations, smiled happily and answered:

"Thank you. Patrick spoke for near an hour in a manner that surprised me, and showed himself well informed on a subject of which I did not know he had any knowledge." But the Judge was not quite able to control a slight tremor of his voice.

The general trend of Henry's speech was remembered by practically all his hearers, and spread abroad, and noted down. In addition here and there one among the audience set down a remembered passage. Captain Thomas

Trevilian, owner of an estate in Hanover County, was among these latter, and it is he who quoted the paragraph concerning the clergy's benevolence. But for years afterwards when some old-timer wished to flatter a newcomer among speakers, he would say "My dear fellow, believe me when I tell you he's almost as good as Patrick Henry, that time he pled the cause against the parsons."

Assuredly the tocsin presaging the Revolution sounded that day in Hanover Court House. Henry had what was then called a "sending voice." Pleasant to those close to him, it was clear to those at a distance. On that day when he was first heard speaking words of freedom, of the right of self-government, the first man in all America so to do, it might have been said of that voice, as it would be said of the first rifle fired at Concord Bridge, that it "was heard around the world."

Instead of winning their cause, the clergy found that they had turned most of Virginia's population against them. The influence of the Established Church, already weakened, was to feel an increasing strain, while the strength of the Dissenters waxed greater. The same was true of the Colony's relations with the King.

The clergy, however, were not ready to give up without trying again. The following year, 1764, Henry's uncle Patrick, through Mr. Peter Lyons, brought suit for the tobacco he claimed to be his due, and again the attorney for the defence was his own nephew. But this suit was continued until after the result of Mr. Camm's case was known, which was shortly to be tried before the General Court at Williamsburg, attended by the Governor and his Council. Appearing for the People in Camm's case was Robert Carter Nicholas, one of the three men who had signed Patrick's appeal to practice law. He won the decision, on the grounds that the Act was in force until disallowed by the King and not subject to retroactive action. Camm next appealed to the Privy Council in England, and until this appeal was settled, the Virginia courts refused to hear any other of the clergy's cases. It was not until 1767 that the Camm appeal was heard by the Privy Council, and refused, the decision of the Virginian General Court being affirmed on the grounds that Mr. Camm's suit was improperly brought. Truth was that by that time every one on both sides of the Atlantic, except possibly Mr. Camm, was heartily sick of the whole question. Also, 1767 was beginning to face issues more important and more dangerous.

Meanwhile Henry's practice had grown tremendously. During the first year after his triumph he entered a hundred and sixty-seven new clients and charged five hundred and fifty new fees. He was, moreover, immediately retained by all those whose cases against the parsons' claims came within the range of his practice. But none other was called, and with the decision of 1767, the plaintiffs' cases were all dismissed. It was the end of that story.

Chapter 4

HE MEETS THE STAMP ACT

$\mathcal{E}$ARLY in the year following his triumph, Patrick bought himself a home in Louisa County, for he was making an excellent income now, owed not a cent, and his practice after the Parsons' Cause increased mightily. An interesting event somewhat later in the spring was his second trip to Williamsburg. On this occasion he went to represent Captain Dandridge before the Assembly's Committee of Privileges and Elections in a contest for the seat of a member, James Littlepage, who had been accused of bribery and corruption. Patrick arrived a few days before the case was called in order to do a bit of sight-seeing, for his previous visit when seeking admission to the bar had carried no spare hours for gadding.

Williamsburg was in the full swing of the season, the Assembly meeting, parties being given, the taverns crowded, the town itself most lovely with blooming gardens and avenues of trees in new leaf. Henry, having not yet learned the value of clothes, came in his somewhat shabby outfit, but as he sauntered about he received an impression of the elegance and color of the society there that delighted him. Carriages drifted by with fair ladies in exquisite costumes, attended by mounted cavaliers in riding suits that were the last cry from London, while even the children wore flowered muslins and lace. No one paid the least attention to him, though one of the Burgesses who later attended the case had this to say:

"I noticed an ill-dressed young man sauntering in the lobby of the capitol who seemed to be a stranger to every one, but I did not trouble to inquire his name. You can imagine my astonishment when, attending the case of the contested election, I found this young man counsel for one of the parties, an astonishment vastly increased when he delivered his argument, which was the finest I'd ever heard."

When Henry was ushered into the room where the Committee sat the members exchanged hoity-toity glances. Who in the world was this young farmer entering among them—with such composure, too? Henry realized the scorn of the aristocratic group, but it did not trouble him. The chairman, Colonel Richard Bland, one of the two gentlemen who had written the letters to the *Gazette* in answer to Mr. Camm, knew who he was, however. Indeed, he and Henry's father had carried on quite a correspondence somewhat earlier in regard to the doctrine of eternal punishment, which John Henry defended, backing his contention by a critical appraisal of the Greek text of the New

Testament. So the Colonel welcomed Patrick with courtesy and the business began.

Dandridge had offered to withdraw in favor of Henry, but this Henry refused. He was not yet ready to enter public life, and also he was eager to be back in his new home, Roundabout, which needed some alterations, and to continue his private practice without a break, especially now, when it was increasing so quickly. But the suggestion that he ought to enter the House of Burgesses appealed strongly. He would keep it in mind.

When his turn came to argue he seems to have had the aristocratic Committee hanging on his words with surprised delight. His theme was the vast importance to man of the right of suffrage, the vital need of guarding it against any chicanery or doubledealing. Into that theme he put a moving eloquence ... which did not prevent his argument from being to at least one of his hearers "the finest I've ever heard." It must have appeared good to all, for he won the case, and after it ended several members present came to shake him by the hand and congratulate this "ill-dressed stranger" upon whom they had looked so coldly a little while earlier.

"You've given me a new conception of an old subject, and not alone new but great," one of them remarked, smiling.

Well content, Patrick rode back to the new home and his family. It was a pleasing place, where there was room for the steadily increasing company of children. He had been married now ten years and had five children, three of them daughters. The eldest was Martha, then John, William, Anne, and Elizabeth. A lively group, and Patrick loved to play with them. At a time when the relationship between parents and children was inclined to be stiff, if not actually formal, young Henry was friends with his. Callers would come in many an evening to find him flat on the floor with the bunch scrambling over him, dancing around him, shrieking with amusement. Or the father might be playing his flute, sometimes making up a jig to set them whirling. The noise was often wonderful.

None had yet gone to school, and all summer the boys ran barefoot. "Give nature its chance first," was Henry's decision. His two brothers-in-law who saw a good deal of the family, used to shout with laughter when they described the children. Thomas Madison especially enjoyed telling yarns of the three boys later on, as they grew up a trifle. "Wild as young colts, barefooted and bareheaded up to fourteen, whooping and hallooing all over the plantation, rough as nature left them." And Samuel Meredith bears out the tale, adding that they and their father were on the most familiar footing, that he treated them as equals, as friends and companions. They'd race toward him, as he returned from hunting, gun in hand, boots and breeches muddy, game-bag slung over his shoulder, screaming questions, "What did you get? Is it a lot of small birds or some big fat partridges? . . ." and he'd laugh at them, shaking his head, making them guess. Or if he'd been out for deer they would run beside his horse, which might be carrying a fine buck slung over the saddle, while Henry walked ahead, the reins over one arm, each child demanding to know where he'd shot it, all laughing at his answers "I got him just as he was strolling into Mr. Moore's parlor," or perhaps "at the crossroads store," or anywhere impossible.

Roundabout, the new home in Louisa County, close to the confluence of Fork and Roundabout creeks, got its

"I got him just as he was strolling into Mr. Moore's parlor."

name from the latter. It was a story-and-a-half house with
a small wing on the north side nicely finished off as a bedroom, and there were two more bedrooms upstairs. Down-
stairs were two more rooms, one small, the other about
eighteen by twenty feet. Plenty of room for the family.
Scattered about were small buildings, a laundry, a kitchen,
pantry, smoke-house, and somewhat farther away the quarters for the Negroes. The site was lovely, atop a hill commanding a fine view of Roundabout Valley, while some
three hundred yards below the house the creek curved to
join the Fork. The house was built between two highways
leading from the mountains to the sea, but far enough
from either to give seclusion. The nearest neighbor was a
farmer, Mr. Perkins.

"Mr. Henry was a great man with fishing rod or gun,
and he enjoyed walking. Never rode to court, told me he
wouldn't miss the walk no matter what the weather. I
never knew a man like him for love of being out-of-door.
He'd be off days at a time, hunting all by himself, sleeping
on the ground, happy as an Indian." So Mr. Perkins. And
walking to court, Patrick always carried his gun, just in
case quail or other small game showed up. With his game-
bag along, he would saunter into the courtroom in time to
take up the first of his cases to be called, looking like any
other farmer as to dress and bearing.

Then, even in small cases, trifles like a summons and
petition for a small sum, he'd speak so that every one listened, and those who had not heard him before would look
astounded. One of the judges remarked that whatever people were doing, they'd drop it when Patrick spoke. "I
could write a letter or draw a declaration or plea without
trouble, as I might in my own office, no matter what was
going on, except when Patrick rose to speak; but let him

rise, and down went my pen, no matter how small the matter, for I couldn't write a word until he'd finished."

It was a cheerful home, Roundabout, as the earlier ones had been and as those that came after were to be, for Patrick and his Sarah both were sunny-tempered. They had taken their scarce years with courage and hope, and now that affairs were steadily to improve, they accepted the fact as naturally as they did the rising sun of a spring morning.

In May, 1765, however, Patrick had to leave his family, his fishing and his hunting, having been elected to the House of Burgesses. William Johnson of Louisa County had been appointed coroner, and resigned his seat in the House, as was obligatory. A man who stood high in that county, William Venable, proposed Henry's name, and he was elected. He took his seat on May 20, and on the 29th, which was also his twenty-ninth birthday, rose to make his famous speech against the Stamp Act.

Swapping Mr. Johnson for Patrick Henry at this particular moment of time was to prove one of those strangely fortunate events at which history loves to point with pride.

Three days after taking his seat Henry had made his first speech to the House, giving it a measure of his boldness and his eloquence. He had been placed on the Committee of Courts of Justice, and spoke against the proposal made by Mr. John Robinson, who was Speaker of the House and Treasurer of the Colony, as well as the accepted head of the landed aristocracy, to establish a public loan office from which money to a certain amount might be lent to individuals, on public account and on good landed security. A motion for such a loan office was brought forward, the point being made that because of "certain unhappy circumstances of the Colony, men of substantial property have contracted debts which, if exacted suddenly, must ruin them and their families, but with a little indul-gence of time, might be paid with ease." This meant that public moneys should be loaned to pay private debts, under the government's wing; moreover, it meant that such loans should be procurable only by the landed, the aristocratic class.

Henry attacked this spirit of favoritism, making it clear that he stood against private privilege, and that he believed it to be the duty of the House to oppose any move of the aristocrats to further their own interests above those of the majority. He demanded, "Sir, is it then proposed to reclaim the spendthrift from his dissipation by filling his pockets with money?" In this speech he roused a hitherto power-ful group to mingled dread and bitter wrath against him. These men were, however, in the minority, and by far the greater part of the House, especially the younger mem-bers, were farmers and small business men. Many of these sided with him, and when Henry ended, their vote killed Mr. Robinson's measure. The Council were for it, how-ever, until a committee of the House, numbering among them Edmund Pendleton, Archibald Cary, Benjamin Har-rison, Lewis Burwell, and a few more, conferred with the members and persuaded them to let it die.

The enthusiasts among the younger members now claimed Henry as one of their own, a small farmer, a young lawyer, yet able to cope with the ablest of the older men long trained in the tactics of the House, long used to having their own way. Here was a man unafraid and strong, a man, moreover, who could speak as no man yet had ever spoken in Virginia.

This first speech not alone raised Henry high in the estimation of the House, but also among several members of the Council. Only a very few there present had ever heard him before; some did not even know his name. But the next speech, against the Stamp Act, hah, there indeed he reached a mark and flamed into a genius that even those who already feared and hated him could never forget nor ever deny!

The Stamp Act had a curious story behind it and one Henry had taken the trouble to study. It was not the work of a day. It had been born two years ago and it spelled tyranny.

The Treaty of Paris, in 1763, ending the French War with England both in Europe and her American colonies, left England in possession of the North American continent so far as it was known at that time, excepting only Florida, Louisiana west of the Mississippi, and New Orleans, riding the east bank of that great stream. Pitt had placed England in the highest place among the nations. But Pitt was forced to resign by King George III, who started, with his coronation three years earlier, to lift the ugly head of Tyranny over all his possessions. The first job was to weaken the power of colonial Assemblies, to force taxes upon them, and to keep a standing army, supported by the colonies, stationed in their chief ports.

But, being rid of the French, the American colonies had no need of any army other than one they could raise easily enough among themselves in case of Indian trouble. During the French war the colonies had put 25,000 men into the field. Moreover, the British soldiers did not know how to fight Indians and proved a bit stiff about learning. To be told to support a standing army of no earthly use, at the time when they were paying on a war debt of more than two and a half millions, was an incredible demand. The association in London known as the Lords of Trade controlled the entire colonial export trade, supplying information and advice to the Secretary of State. But they did not have the power to enforce their recommendations, nor had they any direct access to the King on the matter. This feebleness appeared to keep them in a constant stew of rage, which they took out on the colonies in harsh recommendations. One chief aim of this body was to have the charters under which the colonies were established taken from them. Virginia's charter, granted by James I in 1606, contained this important paragraph:

Also we do, for us, our heirs and successors, declare by these presents that all and every the persons, being our subjects, which shall dwell and inhabit within every or any of the said colonies and plantations, shall have and enjoy all liberties, franchises and immunities within any of our other dominions, to all intents and purposes, as if they had been abiding and born within this our realm of England.

Clear enough. But the colonies had improved on the above, and, led by Virginia, and separated as they were from the motherland by what then was indeed the broad ocean, they early carried their free institutions beyond what was enjoyed in the old world. The elective franchise was more liberal than in England, they had long enjoyed trial by jury, as well as the writ of habeas corpus, which put an end to secret imprisonment. Also, they had necessarily to institute local governments; the Governor was usually appointed by the King, with the power of selecting his own Council, but the Burgesses were elected by the people. Thus each colony, with local differences in detail, possessed the equivalent of England's three-branched government, King, House of Lords, and House of Commons, with a charter granted to each colony assuring them the same freedom as though they had been born and bred in

England, charters brought up to date from time to time, but always maintaining this freedom.

Nothing happier than the colonists of America can be imagined when in 1763 the French war ended. James Otis gave it words when at a meeting in Boston he declared that America had abundant reason to rejoice. "The heathen are driven out, and the Canadians conquered. The British Dominion now extends from sea to sea, and from the great rivers to the ends of the earth. Liberty and knowledge, civil and religious, will co-extend, improved and preserved, to the latest posterity." He added words of praise in regard to the union of Great Britain and her colonies, warning, "What God in His providence has united, let no man dare to pull asunder."

And nothing more miserable and alarmed than the colonists can be imagined when, later in that same year, Parliament renewed the tax on sugar and stiffened the enforcement of the navigation laws, which forced the colonies to send all their produce to Britain, and all in English ships. Every British officer up and down the long coast, whether civil, military, or naval, was henceforth given carte blanche to carry out these orders, and the legality of the seizures of ships accused of illicit traffic was to be judged by appointees of the Crown, constituting the Courts of Admiralty, without benefit of jury. When the case went against the ship owners, the officers who had made the seizure got a large slice of the prize. There was no possibility of appeal because of the immense cost and difficulty of bringing it before the Privy Council in England, the only resource.

The next news from England's King and America's Tyrant was that the colonial charters were to be altered with the effect of weakening the power of their assemblies;

in addition, the tax to be levied for the standing army must be large enough to give England a nice fat residue. It was explained that this was necessary because England was burdened with heavy taxes caused by the late French trouble.

But loud cries of rage from the colonies began to make themselves heard across the ocean, inducing George Grenville, Prime Minister, to drop alteration of the charters out of his scheme of getting much for nothing, and merely to tax, tax, tax.

Grenville told the Colonial Agents in London, Benjamin Franklin among them, that the simplest was the best way, and that it had been agreed upon to impose one tax, to be called the Stamp Tax. Of course if they could think of another method which would produce the same result but which pleased them better, they were free to suggest it, and they were graciously allowed time to ponder, since the tax was not to be imposed before the next session of Commons. Resolutions declaring this purpose were read in Commons on March 9, 1764. The House agreed upon the excellence of the plan; and as to the King, he was pleased as Punch at what he called "the wise regulations which had been established to augment the public revenues, unite the interests of the most distant possessions of the Crown and encourage and secure their commerce with Great Britain."

Somehow it didn't work out that way.

"What," the Colonials said, "about the chartered rights of the Colonies? Are they to count for nothing henceforth?" Everywhere there was discussion and parties were formed, the Tories for the tax, the Whigs against, and they infinitely greater in number although frequently less in wealth. On May 24, 1764, Boston led off with a meeting in

Faneuil Hall instructing their representatives in the Assembly to oppose the tax as subversive of their liberties; also to do their best to get the other colonies to unite in a protest to it. Six days later the Massachusetts Assembly, or as they called it there, General Court, met, with its member from Boston, James Otis, as leading spirit. Most of the colonies, through their Assemblies, issued like protests, embodied in excellent papers. Virginia's meeting occurred in November of that same year, 1764, and on December 18th a committee reported an address to the King, a memorial to the House of Lords, a remonstrance to the House of Commons. Richard Henry Lee wrote the first two, the third was the work of George Wythe. They were good stuff, though rather mild.

The British Ministry, which had not asked the colonies to give reasons why they should not be taxed, but merely allowed them, if so minded, to alter the form without affecting the return, were angry enough to bite. Grenville at once carried the Stamp Act through Parliament. It was passed on February 27th, Commons even refusing to allow the protests of the colonies to be read. On March 8, 1765, it was agreed to by the Lords, and on the 22d the Commission acting for the King, who was going through one of his early periods of insanity, gave the royal assent.

The Act would go into effect the following November. The tax made it obligatory to use the required stamp to validate any number of acts. Marriages were invalid without it, an unstamped obligation was valueless, a ship at sea without her stamps was the prize of the first man to capture her, exchanges in real estate in whatever form must have their stamp or be useless, you could not inherit a bequest without it, all legal operations had to have the papers in the case stamped or not be legal, etc., etc. Turn where you will, thought the horrified colonists, and a stamp stares you in the face. And they weren't tuppenny stamps, either.

The colonists had really believed that the protests they had sent would put an end to the imposition of the tax. They were dumbfounded to find themselves utterly mistaken. The news spread over all the colonies like an evil stench, a horrible depression fell upon the entire populace, but it did not enter the head of any one of their leaders to offer so much as a hint of opposition. "We must submit," said Otis of Massachusetts, shuddering away from the mere idea of resistance. "It is the duty of all, humbly and silently, to acquiesce in the decisions of the supreme legislature. Nine hundred and ninety-nine in a thousand of the colonists will never once entertain a thought but of submission to our Sovereign, and the authority of Parliament in all possible contingencies. They undoubtedly have the right to levy internal taxes on the colonies." Where was the defender of liberty now? Yet Boston reëlected him that May to the Assembly, as also a Mr. Thomas Oliver as Counsellor, although this gentleman had been appointed by England a stamp distributor for Massachusetts. In all the colonies there was a great depression, a feeling of having been badly cheated, yet not one among them made the least attempt to fight the shameless imposition.

The issue appeared settled. It meant no less than that the claim of Parliament to tax the colonies internally without their consent was established, which was simon-pure enslavement. The mass of the people knew they had lost a great right and suffered a great wrong. Yet the men who were the accepted leaders bent the knee and bowed the head.

All but one. One out of the nine-ninety-nine.

Submit, be humble, yield, obey?

That was not Patrick Henry's idea. He had accepted his election to the vacant seat in the Assembly, although the year before he had refused one in order to build up his practice, cultivate his acres, and enjoy his family, because of the Stamp Act, whose every step he had followed. He meant to get in his oar. He saw its danger, and he knew it must be killed. Also, a man of the people, he believed in the people. He felt they'd rally to a bold move, and he intended to have a tussle with that Act, and so give them the chance.

Sitting in a corner of the Hall while routine business was being transacted, he opened his old volume of *Coke upon Littleton*, which he had been studying that morning, and on a blank page or two he set down certain *Resolutions*.

Chapter 5

AND KNOCKS IT OUT

THE Resolutions Henry had scribbled on the blank page of his book were based upon a declaration by Coke that it is against Magna Charta for freemen to be taxed but by their own consent, and that an Act of Parliament against Magna Charta, or common right, or reason, is void.

George Johnston of Fairfax and John Fleming of Cumberland were two members well known to Patrick, and men in whom he believed; before presenting his Resolutions he read them to these two, receiving their unqualified assurance of support.

"They're just what we need, and of all the men I know you are the right one to offer them," George Johnston told him. "You move and I'll second them. Then Fleming and I can speak in their support before you do so."

"I know another man I believe will speak for us, Robert Mumford. Pat, we'll give the House the greatest shock of its history, or I'm mistaken," Fleming added. They laughed together, a thread of excitement in their voices.

Word had got around that Henry was to speak on the Stamp Act that fateful May 29, 1765. As it was drawing to the end of the session most of the hundred and sixteen members had returned to their homes, leaving some say thirty-nine, others forty-one, to finish whatever business was left. All these were present and little time was lost in beginning.

George Johnston took the floor. He was a man of high character, known as a champion of liberty, a lawyer, a scholar. He moved that the house go into Committee of the Whole to consider the Stamp Act. Henry seconded. Carried. The clerk put the Speaker's mace on its shelf under the table. Mr. Robinson left his seat as presiding officer, Peyton Randolph, Attorney-General, occupying it. The Resolutions were read to the Committee. All was now ready. Mr. Robinson returned to his seat as Speaker of the House. Preliminaries were over.

Henry then offered the House, one by one, his Resolutions.

He was a man always careless of his notes and speeches, but this time he made a copy of his five Resolutions, with an endorsement written on the back of the same sheet of paper, enclosed in a sealed envelope, to be opened by his executors after his death. He considered them, and the effect they had produced, so important as to merit this care.

This was particularly fortunate because of a great deal of confusion later in regard to exactly how many resolutions were offered, their exact wording, and which among them did not pass.

Here is Henry's own copy of them:

1: *Resolved,* That the first adventurers and settlers of this his Majesty's colony and dominion brought with them, and transmitted to their posterity, and all other his Majesty's subjects since inhabiting in this his Majesty's said colony, all the privileges, franchises and immunities that have at any time been held, enjoyed and possessed by the people of Great Britain.

2: *Resolved,* That by two royal charters, granted by James I, the colonists aforesaid are declared entitled to all the privileges, liberties and immunities of denizens and natural born subjects, to all intents and purposes, as if they had been abiding and were born within the realm of England.

3: *Resolved,* That the taxation of the people by themselves, or by persons chosen by themselves to represent them, who only can know what taxes the people are able to bear, and the easiest mode of raising them, and are equally affected by such taxes themselves, is the distinguishing characteristick of British freedom, and without which the ancient Constitution cannot subsist.

4: *Resolved,* That his Majesty's liege people of this most ancient colony have uninterruptedly enjoyed the right of being thus governed by their own Assembly in the article of their taxes and internal police, and that the same hath never been forfeited or any other way given up, but hath been constantly recognized by the kings and people of Great Britain.

5: *Resolved, therefore,* That the General Assembly of this colony have the only and sole exclusive right and power to lay taxes and impositions upon the inhabitants of this colony, and that every attempt to vest such power in any person or persons whatsoever, other than the General Assembly aforesaid, has a manifest tendency to destroy British as well as American freedom.

There followed, on the reverse of the page, this note:

The within resolutions passed the House of Burgesses in May, 1765. They formed the first opposition to the Stamp Act and the scheme of taxing America by the British Parliament. All the colonies, either through fear, or want of opportunity to form an opposition, or from influence of some kind or other, had remained silent. I had been for the first time elected a Burgess a few days before, was young, inexperienced, unacquainted with the forms of the House and the members that composed it. Finding the men of weight averse to opposition, and the commencement of the tax at hand, and that no person was like to step forward, I determined to venture, and alone, unadvised and unassisted, on a blank leaf of an old law book, wrote the within. Upon offering them to the House violent debates ensued, many threats were uttered, and much abuse cast on me from the party for submission. After a long and warm contest the resolutions passed by a very small majority, perhaps of one or two only. The alarm spread through America with astonishing quickness, and the Ministerial party was overwhelmed. The great point of resistance to British taxation was universally established in the colonies. This brought on the war which finally separated the two countries and gave independence to ours. Whether this will prove a blessing or a curse will depend upon the use our people make of the blessings which a gracious God hath bestowed on us. If they are wise, they will be great and happy. If they are of a contrary character, they will be miserable. Righteousness alone can exalt them as a nation. Reader! whoever thou art, remember this; and in thy sphere practice virtue thyself and encourage it in others.

P. Henry.

These five, Henry witnesses, were passed by the House. There appears to have been a sixth, which ran in this wise, and was lost in committee:

Resolved, That any person who shall, by speaking or writing, assert or maintain that any person or persons, other than the General Assembly, have any right or power to impose or lay any taxation on the people here, shall be deemed an enemy of his Majesty's colony.

There was even talk that the above was number seven, and that number six resolved, "That his Majesty's liege people, the inhabitants of this colony, are not bound to yield obedience to any law or ordinance whatever, designed to impose any taxation whatever upon them, other than the laws and ordinances of the General Assembly aforesaid." But it is extremely unlikely that Henry would have written two resolves so nearly identical as these two. There probably was a sixth one, which did not pass the Committee and was not offered to the House.

The intense excitement these five resolves roused and the violent opposition of Messrs. Randolph, Bland, Pendleton, and Wythe with most of the remaining old members were something the House had never before experienced. One by one they were read, assailed, defended; Johnston, a man of sound reasoning powers, Mumford, and Fleming all supported them. One by one they passed until the fifth was reached. Jefferson, who watched and listened from the doorway opening into the lobby, says the debate on this "was most bloody." And now Henry spoke. Again Jefferson, who never denied Henry's powers as an orator, comments, saying he "heard the splendid display of Mr. Henry's talents as a popular orator. They were great indeed, such as I have never heard from any other man. He appeared to me to speak as Homer wrote."

Henry's fiercest opponent was the Speaker, John Robinson, who, since the defeat of the loan measure, cherished a bitter hatred against him. He had more reason for this than was known, at the time.

There are, alas, no more than snatches of the speech

preserved, that "torrent of eloquence" which swept its speaker to success. But apparently none forgot the ever-famous ending:

"Caesar had his Brutus, Charles the First his Cromwell, and George the Third—" "Treason!" screamed Mr. Robinson, and "Treason, treason!" sounded from all parts of the room.

Henry, never faltering an instant, fixed his eyes, that appeared to flash a blue flame, on the Speaker's face, and rising it seemed to a loftier height, slowly and with a thrilling emphasis reached his conclusion "—may profit by their example. If *this* be treason, make the most of it."

The fifth Resolution was carried by a single vote.

Past Jefferson, still standing breathless in the doorway, as the members were told and declared by the chair, rushed Peyton Randolph, exclaiming, as he reached the lobby: "By God, I would have given five hundred guineas for a single vote!" For had he had that vote, the house would have been divided, the Speaker, being in the chair, would have cast the deciding vote, and every one knew what that would have been. As it was, Mr. Robinson, in his velvet and ruffles, leaned back in the great chair, standing on its dais, under its red velvet canopy, and stared around the room where the winners were cheering.

Henry had taken the lead of the House from Wythe and Pendleton, Bland and Randolph, and they sensed it.

Shocked, horrified, Governor Fauquier dissolved the Assembly on June 1st, presently writing the following letter to the Lords of Trade:

I dissolved the Assembly, after passing all the bills but one ... the four Resolutions, which I now have the honor to inclose to your Lordships, will show your Lordships the reason for my conduct and I hope, justify it. I will relate the whole proceedings to your Lordships in as concise a manner as I am able.

On Wed., May 29th, just at the end of the session, when most of the members had left the town, there being but 39 present of 116, of which the House of Burgesses now consists, a motion was made to take into consideration the Stamp Act, a copy of which had crept into the House; and in a committee of the whole five resolutions were reported and agreed to by the House, the number being as before in the committee; the greatest majority being 22 to 17; for the fifth resolution, 20 to 19 only. On Friday, the 31st, there having happened a small altercation in the House, there was an attempt to strike all the resolutions off the journals. The 5th, which was thought the most offensive, was accordingly struck off, but it did not succeed as to the other four. I am informed the gentlemen had two other resolutions in their pocket, but finding the difficulty they had in carrying the fifth, which was by a single vote, and knowing them to be more virulent and inflammatory, they did not produce them.

The most strenuous opposers of this rash heat were the late Speaker, the King's Attorney, and Mr. Wythe; but they were overpowered by the young and giddy members. In the course of the debates I have heard that very indecent language was used by Mr. Henry, a young lawyer who had not been above a month a member of the House, and who carried all the young members with him. So that I hope I am authorized at least in saying that there is no cause to doubt whether this would have been the sense of the colony, if most of their representatives had done their duty by attending to the end of the session. [*Indecent* held the sense of *improper* as we use it in that connotation today.]

Ah, the young and giddy, the bold and the free! How much we owe you in this old world of ours!

Henry left Williamsburg for home the day following his victory, walking along broad Duke of Gloucester Street, which runs from the Palace to the College, in earnest talk with Paul Carrington, who himself had only entered the

House as a delegate from Charlotte, on May 25th. The two men were friends from the start, and for life.

Hardly was Patrick out of sight before attempts were started to have the Resolutions passed by the House killed. Jefferson, returning to the House next day, found Colonel Peter Randolph, a member of the Council, seeking frantically through old journals of the proceedings of the House, for a precedent he believed would permit the expunging of the vote, and so an end to the matter. Evidently he did not find such a precedent. But three days afterwards the manuscript journal of the proceedings mysteriously disappeared, whether lost or stolen—you can take your choice. In the printed journal only the first four Resolutions appeared, but the one printer in Williamsburg was known to be completely under the thumb of Governor Fauquier. The *Virginia Gazette* later published not only the five, but the sixth, which had not passed.

It mattered not. The resolutions were spread over the entire chain of colonies with startling speed, welcomed everywhere by a flame of fury and revolt. By August riots occurred against the selected distributors of the stamps. Up in New York Lieutenant-Governor Golden endeavored to quell those occurring under his jurisdiction. The rioters seized his carriage, put two effigies, one of Golden, the other a terrific-looking Devil, into the seat, dragging it through shouting crowds and to ever wilder hurrahs burning it in a public square. Newspapers everywhere came out with violent articles, while the *Pennsylvania Journal* published a grinning skull and crossbones, with the caption in bold-faced type *The Times are Dreadful, Dismal, Doleful, Dolorous—and Dollarless*. Massachusetts was not left behind. First the citizens of Boston hanged the effigy of the stamp distributor for the colony, Mr. Oliver; the gentleman at once resigned the position. Next they sacked the house of Chief Justice Hutchinson, known to stand firmly on the side of Parliament. Also, they hunted out crates of the stamps and burned them, all of this to considerable noise and rough-housing. Fourteen other towns scattered through that colony kicked up rackets of varying ferocity. Mr. Otis remarked that "one single Act of Parliament has set the people thinking in six months more than they have ever done in their whole lives before."

Very properly, nonetheless, he did not approve the rows; he was clear that window smashing and burning effigies got you nowhere. An earlier plan of his, to have the colonies hold a convention to discuss the Act, had flopped. Now it began to take hold, and nine of the colonies sent representatives. One, Christopher Gadsden, came all the way from South Carolina, passing through Virginia to find that Governor Fauquier had forbidden any representation from that colony. Otis was the principal speaker and Gadsden made a splendid speech, saying he did not want to see any more petitions sent to England. "We should stand upon the common grounds of those natural rights which we all feel and know as men, and as descendents of Englishmen." He urged united action, telling his audience that if the different colonies began to act differently in this great cause, "all will be over with the whole. There ought to be no New Englander, nor other colonial, but all of us Americans."

But the convention did not amount to much, being of a timid and hesitating temper, behaving, as they put it, "with all due subordination to that august body, the Parliament" in spite of its "manifest tendency to subvert the rights and interests of the people." Fourteen resolutions were passed, amounting to the assertion that they claimed the right of self-taxation and trial by jury, and winding up with the declaration, "We glory in being subjects of the best of Kings," which even to-day makes one feel slightly sick.

But Henry's name, and copies of his Resolutions, were published all over the land, and everywhere wildly hailed by the people. His bold, magnificent retort to the charge of treason was widely quoted. Everywhere societies were formed calling themselves the Sons of Liberty, largely composed of the laboring classes, led by men of strength and intelligence, and becoming the chief force of popular demonstrations against the government.

The Stamp Act was due to take effect in November.

It never did so. On March 18, 1766, four months after that date, King George signed its repeal. Pitt had got out of bed to urge this repeal on Commons, for trade had suffered badly, since the colonists refused to send anything to England or to buy anything from her. People were becoming alarmed, and rumors that large bodies of soldiers would have to be sent across seas if the colonists were to be forced to pay the tax were hard to down. So the King signed, and that night, in his capital of London, streets were illuminated, bells were rung, the crowds cheered.

As for America, when the news came, the country went wild. The colonies had won. The tumult and the dread were ended. Freedom had triumphed.

And why? Because a man of thirty, for the first time a member of any legislative assembly and a stranger to all but a very few in the House, after only ten days of experience there, had proposed and carried against the furious opposition of practiced and able men, till then the unquestioned leaders of the Assembly, a handful of resolutions, daring as they were clear and simple, backing them

tion as Chief Justice of the Court of Common Pleas, he boldly maintained the right of the colonies to resist the tax. "My position is this—I repeat it and I will maintain it to my last hour—taxation and representation are inseparable ... for what is a man's own is absolutely his own; no man hath a right to take it from him without his consent, either expressed by himself or a representative; whoever attempts to do it attempts an injury; whoever does it commits a robbery; he throws down and destroys the distinction between liberty and slavery. Taxation and representation are co-eval with and essential to this constitution."

There were others of a like mind, and perhaps even stronger to many of the representatives than the fight for the rights of man, was the piercing shriek from London's merchants that "We are being ruined!"

So the Act was repealed. But Parliament was not squelched. It gave itself a loophole. The repeal was merely an act of expediency. The House went on record as holding the opinion that King and Parliament "had, hath, and of right ought to have full power and authority to make laws and statutes of sufficient force and validity to bind the colonies and people of America subjects to the crown of Great Britain, in all cases whatsoever."

In America, although the colonies now looked forward cheerfully to a prosperous and decent union with Great Britain, there were some who doubted. Was the fight really won? Was the freedom they claimed surely theirs? Unless Parliament changed its attitude and foreswore its claims, it seemed to these men that danger lay ahead. Among them was Patrick Henry.

When the Burgesses met again, which was not until November, 1766, their first duty was to select a new

Speaker, Mr. John Robinson having died some time earlier. Mr. Robinson had been a man of great wealth, among the very richest in Virginia. He was also generous and given to lending money to any of his group who needed it "for the time." Gradually, being Treasurer of Virginia, he began to use the public moneys for this largesse, trusting on the securities given him to replace what he had borrowed. But by degrees more and more public moneys were thus used, until the deficit grew so great he realized that it could not much longer remain hid from the public. If the plan to establish a Public Loan had carried, all the debts due Robinson could have been transferred, and his use of the Treasury funds never discovered. Henry, when he fought the measure, had no knowledge of this fact, but simply did not like the favoritism it made possible.

At the opening of the new session Richard Henry Lee, being assured of Patrick's assistance, offered a bill separating the two offices of Speaker and Treasurer. This was heavily contested, Edmund Pendleton leading the opposition. But Henry carried it through, establishing his place as the leader of the popular party. Henry's claim was that the two offices should never have been united, and in his speech, which exposed the absurdity of uniting them, as well as the simplicity of separating them, he spoke with a calm composure, with a sound sense and a felicity of phrase that won over many on the opposing side. One of Henry's marked characteristics was that he never tried to make a mountain out of a molehill, to fake a passion where one was neither needed nor felt. His speech was successful, the motion was carried, and a committee appointed to examine the accounts of the late Treasurer. It was then that the huge deficit was discovered, amounting to over a hundred thousand pounds. A few in the House must have known of this, but for most it was a severe shock and grief. Robinson had held his two posts for twenty-five years, and was a man really beloved, and by no means only by those he had befriended.

But before all this came out Peyton Randolph had become the Speaker, and Robert C. Nicholas the Treasurer.

Lee greatly appreciated what Henry's speech had done, the friendship between the two men remaining fast until Lee's death in 1794, although they frequently differed in their political opinions.

This session of the Assembly was enthusiastically patriotic. All those who had supported Henry's resolutions on the Stamp Act were returned, except a few who did not ask for reëlection. Of those who had opposed him, some changed their minds and were returned, others lost their seats. He was easily the most popular man in the House, and all the forward-looking were with him.

Another item in regard to the Speaker was the voting of a salary to the man appointed to the post. This was to "maintain the Chair's dignity," but it was also excellent for the patriot cause, since it automatically made the Speaker the servant of the House, and not of the Governor.

Once all this was settled, the first business before the House was the passing of a bill for the purpose of erecting a statue to King George III and an obelisk to those men in Parliament who had fought for the colonies' cause. Next a new county, west of and adjoining Halifax County, and bounded on the north by the Roanoke River, was set off and named Pittsylvania, in honor of freedom's great champion, its parish carrying the name Camden, honoring

Baron Camden. And to finish off, *Addresses* were voted to both King and Parliament, which, like those in the rest of the colonies, expressed loyalty and attachment.

When the session ended in December, however, nothing had been done about either the proposed statue or the obelisk, which were dished until the next session, and never heard of again. So America lost her one chance of having a king's statue set up within her boundaries.

Two other Acts were passed by the Assembly before it adjourned, probably moved by Henry and certainly supported by him. One was the laying of an additional tax on the importation of Africans by the slave trade, a source, this trade, of much money to England. The second exempted Quakers from military service, and was a first strong step toward religious tolerance, for which Henry would do great work as time passed and which had always appealed to him.

Every one went home and the stage was almost immediately set for the next act. Again the leading actor was the irrepressible Mr. TAX.

The Assembly was not to meet again until March, 1768, the Governor proroguing it from time to time, not liking the increasing irritation of the people. During that period Patrick was busy in many ways.

For one thing there was his father, a grand old man, but infinitely better as a scholar than a man of business. Henry had helped him out of financial difficulties several times, and it was as return for these, as well as for a new loan, that John Henry had deeded Roundabout to his son. At present he was running a classical school for boys at his home, Mount Brilliant, with some twenty-odd pupils, and doing nicely. But something which interested him far more, and interested Patrick too, was what he called a

Memorial, with excellent and very modern suggestions, which he had submitted to the Assembly, and which had been read to the House of Burgesses on November 10th.

Judge Henry's theme was the great advantage to the colony if an accurate map of the region were made, with careful surveying of all roads, their measurement and marking. "For one thing, Pat," he told his son, "the veniremen and witnesses who are called to attend the General Court would be able to collect their just traveling dues, neither too much nor yet too little. As it is, many of them are reduced to guesswork."

Another of the items suggested in Judge Henry's *Memorial* was the benefit to be had if the shoals in Chesapeake Bay and the rivers flowing into it should be correctly marked. (Incidentally, that had to wait for another century, when the great Naval expert Matthew Fontaine Maury did the job.) But first must come the mapping of the entire colony, with separate maps of each of its several counties.

Here Judge Henry had himself done a very excellent piece of work, with such assistance as he could come by. He wanted this map published with, as he put it, "the most curious and entertaining observations relative to the country, its Productions, number of inhabitants, Rarities, Trade, and whatever else may be judged proper to be inserted in the Vacant Places of such Maps."

Quite a number of men both in the House and in Judge Henry's own county were much interested in these plans, but nothing came of them then. The country was moving toward new hazards, feeling was mounting, there was no time to take up ideas, however sensible, not directly associated with the political situation. Patrick, of course, agreed as to the usefulness of such maps and information; moreover, young Henry had plans of his own in regard to developing Virginia's resources in several directions. He set these down in an article which is the first of his writings to be preserved, written in 1766, before going to the meeting of the Assembly, and very likely he talked over some of them with friends like Lee and Carrington. Religious tolerance was one, another the necessity of halting the importation of slaves, both later to appear in the Acts passed by the Burgesses.

In the same paper he discussed the financial situation of Pennsylvania as opposed to that of Virginia. "How comes it," he writes, "that the lands in Pennsylvania are five times the value of ours?" and answers, "Pennsylvania is the country with the most extensive privileges, with few slaves. A Dutch, Irish or Scotch emigrant finds there his religion, his priest, his language, his manners, everything but that poverty and oppression he left at home. Take an instance nearer us. [He is speaking of the western lands of Virginia, beyond the Blue Ridge.] The country beyond the mountains is settled on a plan of economy very different from ours. Europeans, instead of Africans, till the lands, and manufacture. The tax to the established church is scarcely felt. The people brought their priests with them. The lands in some parts are almost as dear as at Williamsburg, and notwithstanding the many disadvantages arising from situation, they are the most flourishing parts of Virginia, and this in a few years... I agree entirely with those who insist on the necessity for home manufactures. We differ in the means of producing them. To what purpose do we offer premiums, when experience tells us no one will obtain them? ... The present inhabitants of the colonies must manufacture under great disadvantage, for the countries with whom we are connected send continual supplies to our doors, offering to take in barter those commodities the culture of which we understand. If attempts are made we find the many difficulties too great to be conquered. It must ever be so till we have procured great numbers of skilful artists. A planter willing to go upon the new plan cannot have a spinner of wool or flax, a tanner, a shoe-maker, a weaver, a fuller, etc., in his own family. He must travel continually great distances to find these several peo-ple, and when he hath found them they are bunglers, and extravagant in their charges. He is rid of this trouble and perplexity by going to a store."

All this reveals that Henry was constantly occupied with the needs of his colony, its lacks, its prejudices. He wanted men to come to Virginia who could make the things which, instead, the colony was forced to buy in England. In rela-tion to the importation of slaves he insists, "Is there a man so degenerate as to wish to see his country the gloomy re-treat of slaves? No! While we may, let us people our lands with men who secure our internal peace, and make us respectable abroad; who will contribute their influence and stablish in posterity the benefit of the British Constitu-tion." In regard to Virginia's attitude toward religious tolerance, Henry wrote:

When I say that the article of religion is deemed a trifle by our people in general I assert a known truth. But when we suppose that the poorer sort of European emigrants set as light by it, we are greatly mistaken. The free exercise of re-ligion hath stocked the northern part of the continent with inhabitants; and though Europe hath in great measure adopted a more moderate policy, yet the profession of Prot-estantism is extremely inconvenient in many places there. But a Calvinist, a Lutheran, or a Quaker who hath felt these in-conveniences in Europe, sails not to Virginia, where they are felt perhaps in a greater degree.

John Shelton, Patrick's father-in-law, needing cash, had sold him 3,000-odd acres of wild land lying along Moccasin Creek and the Holston River. Late in the spring of '67 Patrick got hold of William Christian, who was to become his brother-in-law, and of his own brother William, now married and who had given up the wildness of his youth, the three riding off to spend a fortnight looking over the newly acquired country, camping, shooting, fishing, as well as planning the development of the land and studying the best sites for future homes. Henry intended to have farms ready for his sons as they grew to manhood, and moreover he liked buying land, preferring to spend money that way when he had it to spend. His law practice, which had fallen off because of the anxious political situation, was again in full swing. The holiday over, he was busy in various courthouses with law business. But now an increasing anger against the goings-on in Parliament began to spread over the country.

Even before the people's joy over the repeal of the Stamp Act two years ago had died down, the Billeting Act was passed by Parliament, as well as an order commanding the colonists to indemnify all those who had suffered loss of property in the rioting. The billeting expense fell hardest on New York, which had to feed, house, and pay the greatest number of British soldiers; but there were other colonies which had to foot bills for these unwanted guests. The various Assemblies in obeying these orders from Parliament smoothed their rebellious feelings to some extent by passing resolutions complying with the demands, certainly, but as though they were passed of their own free will and because they were considered best for the general good.

The Chancellor of the Exchequer, Charles Townsend,

in London, as early as January 26, 1767, defied the Americans in a speech to the House, declaring, "I laugh at the absurd distinction between internal and external taxes. It is a distinction without a difference; it is perfect nonsense. A distinction without a difference, except to the Americans—" here he looked up at the gallery where the colonies' agents were sitting, adding—"I speak this aloud, that all of you in the galleries may hear me; and after this I do not expect to have my statue erected in America."

Hardly stuff to soothe the savage American breast! In May, Townsend delivered another whack, proposing that the Assembly in New York should be forbidden to legislate until that colony had complied with the Billeting Act. New York was making a fuss over the heavy burden, withholding payments, demanding a different arrangement. In this speech Townsend also announced that he wanted port duties collected in America on wine, oil, fruits, glass, paper, lead, colors, and TEA. And apparently it was that last item which did not break the camel's back, but caused the creature to shake off the whole pack and stand free.

Two men, Thomas Pownall, who had been Royal Governor of Massachusetts, and Edmund Burke, who had served as a clerk in the Colonial Office and knew well the temper of the colonists, warned Commons, which had warmly applauded Townsend, that the colonies would not allow themselves to be taxed by Parliament.

These words of truth were merely laughed at. All the taxes proposed were adopted, to take effect in the coming November. What was more, a Board of Trade was appointed by King George to enforce the new Act, the members to live in America and be appointed by himself. The Board was armed with the right of search and seizure at their own discretion, together with authority to call up

the Army and Navy stationed in the colonies, to support
their decisions. More and worse, these men were to be
exempt from prosecution.

And then Mr. Townsend died.

All through these outrages the colonists did not sit quiet.
Many among the leading men both north and south wrote
articles to the papers, denouncing the new tyranny. In
November, 1767, John Dickinson of Pennsylvania published a series of articles under the pseudonym *A Farmer*,
republished in newspapers all over the country, and in
the following month Samuel Adams drew up a letter for
the Massachusetts Assembly, to be sent to their Agent in
London, together with an Address to the Ministry and a
Petition to the King, clearly setting forth the rights of the
colonists and asking for the repeal of the late oppressive
Acts of Parliament. At the same time he wrote a Circular
Letter which was sent to all the other colonies asking them
to get together in an effort to obtain the repeal of the
obnoxious Acts, and to make suggestions of their own as
to the best way to proceed.

In Virginia Indian trouble was starting again, and Governor Fauquier, who had prorogued the Assembly so
steadily, was obliged to call the members to meet on the
last day of March, 1768, to take the necessary measures to
guard the Colony. Before the date set, however, Fauquier
fortunately died, and a Virginian, John Blair, President of
the Council, became acting Governor until Britain's new
appointee should arrive.

Petitions from a number of counties, as well as the
Adams Circular Letter, were taken up at once by the Burgesses. The Indian trouble faded out of sight. The House
adopted unanimously its own messages to King, Lords,
and Commons, written in more trenchant phrases than

those coming from Massachusetts. The Speaker was then directed to forward their proceedings to the other colonies, at the same time asking for a "united, firm but decent opposition to every measure affecting their rights."

Destiny was on the march.

Through all this business Patrick Henry played his strong part. "It was to him that we were indebted for the unanimity which prevailed among us," Jefferson conceded in later life, when he so often spoke untruly and unkindly of Henry. For Henry, fiery patriot that he was, great orator, had what was infinitely valuable as well, a marvelous power of conciliation, a tact that won men over to his opinion. In conversation he was interested in the other man's point of view, considerate, yet always holding with courage to his own conviction. It was not only on his feet, exercising the bright flame of his genius, that he won over his opponents, but in the endless personal contacts in the House, on the streets of Williamsburg, in his own or another's home. His influence in the Assembly was very great, but only at selected moments conspicuous.

Chapter 7

RISING TEMPERATURE

FAUQUIER had been seriously ill intermittently for almost two years before his death, during which time John Blair, as President of the Council, had taken over his duties. He was a kinsman of the James Blair who had founded William and Mary College, in 1695, and served as its head for fifty years till his death. Also it was because of the building of the college and the success it achieved that when Jamestown was abandoned three years later the capital was built in that salubrious and lovely part of Virginia. The name of Blair meant a good deal, therefore, to Williamsburg, and it was a fortunate thing that in the present troubled time as wise and fine a man as John Blair was at the head of the government. He had, of course, thrown all his influence into the side of freedom, and his backing had made possible the strong support to Massachusetts and the vigor of the messages sent to England.

The Assembly ended its session before the end of April. In June the Massachusetts Assembly met, with British troops in the city of Boston, and her warships in the Bay. Britain had sent orders that Massachusetts must rescind Samuel Adams' Letter, at the same time commanding the rest of the colonies to "treat it with contempt." The first act of the Assembly in Boston was a cool refusal to obey, passing by a large majority vote, upon which it was immediately dissolved by the Governor. The rest of the Assemblies treated, not the Letter, but the Royal Order, with contempt.

These two orders had been sent to America after the Ministry in London received a copy of Adams' Circular Letter from the Governor of Massachusetts, who dispatched with it a note of his own saying that he took it to be no less than an attempt to form a Confederacy of the Colonies, and that it was undoubtedly intended to inflame the already dangerous spirit being shown. The Secretary of the Colonies, Lord Hillsborough, laid the papers before the Cabinet on April 15, 1768, which, outraged, declared the Adams' Letter was a direct incentive to rebellion. When the poisonous document was read to the King he actually puffed with royal rage. Something must be done and that quickly, to teach these damned Americans a lesson in proper behavior to the best of Monarchs.

The outcome was the two orders, one to Massachusetts, the other to the remaining colonies, which had just been defied. News traveled slowly in those days, and it was not until November that Parliament met to be told the shocking fact that the colonies had ignored Britain's behests. It was time to be really stern with them.

After considerable discussion an Act of Henry VIII was dug up from under the ashes of time, where it had long lain forgotten. It had not been too good even in its own day, and it tasted a lot worse in 1768. This Act provided that all and any committing treason outside of England against the King should be arrested and brought to England for trial. This Act was now to be enforced against Massachusetts, at present the arch criminal among the colonies. Those men to be declared guilty were instantly to be arrested and brought to London, probably in chains.

A few cautious spirits warned that this might anger the other colonies, and to placate them it was decided that some of the Duty Acts they were making such a row over should be repealed.

In this same month of November the new royal governor, Norborne Berkeley, Baron de Botetourt, reached Virginia. England had made quite an effort to please Virginia in her selection of Botetourt, a particularly pleasant, courteous, and wealthy man sure to make himself liked. England had, however, overlooked the fact that the new Governor was not only a pleasing, but a liberty-loving man, and that his sympathies lay with the colonies, and not with their oppressors.

It had also been decided, as another sop to her favorite colony, that the baron would really be the Governor, and not, as hitherto, merely the Lieutenant-Governor. For until now, through all the years, the true governor was some man the Ministry or the King wanted to reward with a fat plum—especially since its cost was borne not by England, but by Virginia. This man would be appointed governor, but was not required to do anything more than delegate his office to a second man, the lieutenant-governor, who would therefore journey to America and there abide and rule. He too had a salary, also paid by Virginia. Now this was to be changed. Botetourt came as full governor, and met a splendid reception in Williamsburg. He brought with him a magnificent carriage with six white horses to draw it, returning the visits made him in high state, but also with a friendly simplicity that won people to him. A long-bodied, short-legged man, on the plump side, with a bald top to his head, otherwise fringed with sparse white hair worn in a pigtail, he was wont to wear silk or velvet coats and much ruffle at wrists and neck, while, to the amusement of the town, often showing large holes in his white stockings.

Botetourt's first act as Governor was to refuse to issue writs of assistance to the hated Revenue Act, which instantly made him popular all over the Colony. Before leaving England he had been assured that many, if not all the taxes were to be repealed; after conferring with John Blair and the Council he agreed with them that the refusal in regard to the writs was necessary. It was also agreed that the Assembly should be called to meet in May. Meanwhile the new Governor could get acquainted with Virginia's leading men and learn the problems which were now facing the Colony.

During this period Patrick Henry had been thoroughly occupied. During the last half of 1768 a vicious persecution was started and carried on against the Baptists, who had been preaching throughout the Colony in people's houses or various meeting places with considerable energy and success. This roused a bitter hostility among many of the clergy of the Established Church, who presently saw to it that numbers of these preachers were arrested as disturbers of the peace.

Henry's attitude of tolerance toward religious beliefs, differing from the Episcopalian, but nonetheless Christian, was well known, and many of the men arrested, either through those who sympathized with their teachings, or on their own, secured his services. Indeed, Patrick offered to do his best for any of the accused within reach of his practice. He traveled from one county to another defending the Baptists, two of these colonies being Caroline and Chesterfield. At the Caroline Court Edmund Pendleton was on the Bench; there were several of the preachers in prison there, and Pendleton justified this by asserting that these men were "worshipping God according to the dictates of their own conscience!" This could not be endured in Caroline County—until Henry got to work. Archibald Cary's county, Chesterfield, was also extremely active in throwing Baptists into jail, and here Henry went on another rescue mission. Cary, like Pendleton, had done his best, in vain, to kill Patrick's great Resolutions, which put an end to the Stamp Act, and again the two were forced to yield before the vigor and brilliance of his onslaught. From then on Patrick always held himself in readiness to defend without charge any man in trouble because of his religious convictions. In Chesterfield County he got the necessary order to liberate a Mr. Weatherfield, who had been three months in the jail. Weatherfield was a poor man, unable to pay the jail fees which were then charged to all prisoners, for the privilege of eating and sleeping in the place, so there was nothing to be done but stay on, of course increasing the liability. Fortunately Henry heard of this and paid the fees himself, forbidding his name to be disclosed. Some twenty years later when Henry moved to

Charlotte County the preacher at the near-by Baptist church proved to be this Mr. Weatherfield. One day as the two men were talking over the old, intolerant times, Weatherfield related how he came to be freed, and Henry confessed: "I'm the man you've been wondering about."

"You! Then at last I can repay my benefactor. I knew you'd got the order for my release—but not that you'd made it possible."

Henry laughed, telling him to put the money into the poor-box.

"Those were strange days, Mr. Weatherfield. Here was the Colony fighting, or at least getting ready to fight for freedom, yet not hesitating to play the part of tyrant. Man's an unaccountable creature, filled with contradictions, which is, of course, why he's so interesting a study."

Early in this year Patrick's favorite sister, Anne, married William Christian, who had accompanied Henry on the camping trip to look over the wild lands. Christian, a captain of the Second Virginia Regiment who before he was twenty had fought under Colonel Byrd in the French War, was the son of a Staunton merchant who was also one of Patrick's clients. Now he had been in Henry's law office for more than a year, studying. Every one in both families was pleased at the match.

Toward the latter end of 1768 the Patrick Henry family moved back to Hanover. For one thing, Henry felt he wanted to be nearer Williamsburg, for another, his father was beginning to show his age. Henry expected to spend more of his time at the Capital, since he was to be admitted to the bar of the General Court, the highest rank a lawyer could attain in Virginia, some time in 1769. Also, Roundabout, though it had many advantages, was practically out of reach of Hanover for his wife, yet all her friends and relatives were there. By the beginning of November the move was made. Having got the family settled, Henry went to Williamsburg on a short visit. Botetourt had arrived, and a number of the men who were sympathetic with Henry's plans and projects had gone there to help welcome the new Governor. It was a good time to talk things over.

At this moment, in England, the scheme to arrest the "traitors" in Massachusetts had been agreed to, but of course the colonies knew nothing of that yet, nor did Botetourt, who had left England before the House of Commons met. So far the revenue acts were not in force, and it seemed likely they would be abandoned.

But Henry thought it highly possible that England was by no means through disciplining the colonies. Carrington was of a like mind. Both, with several others of Henry's party, decided that vigilance was necessary. They did not forget that Parliament, even in repealing the taxes, had kept the tax on tea, and with it her claim that the right to tax remained with Commons.

"So long as the House of Commons agrees with the Ministry that it has the right to tax us without representation, just so long we'll have to insist that they have no such right, under no circumstances—and I mean none—" Henry turned his brilliant gaze on Richard Henry Lee, who, with Carrington, was strolling beside him toward the Raleigh Tavern for the midday meal before Patrick started homeward. "Massachusetts has been singled out for punishment just now because of Mr. Adams. But we are as apt as any other colony to be the next on their list."

Lee nodded:

"We've won the first bout. We'll never yield the next."

"Amen," returned Patrick. "The struggle for freedom is endless. Our forefathers fought for it, can we do less?"

Henry was no longer the carelessly clad man of the past. On this day he wore a plum-colored silk coat, black silk breeches, a dark wig tied in a bag, buckled shoes, and white stockings. His three-cornered hat became him well and from under it his deep-set blue eyes with their long, dark lashes under heavy reddish eyebrows flashed as he spoke. He was happy with these two friends as he strode along the lovely tree-bordered street with its box-hedged gardens, planted with flowers whose first seeds and bulbs had been brought from England. At this season the trees were bare but the gardens still richly green, and the sunshine, with the help of the tree boughs, drew charming patterns of shadow on the ground. The day was fine and mild, the street well filled with men and women smartly clad, with Negroes hurrying on errands, or gathered in small groups chattering and laughing. Brick houses with white-pillared porticoes and trimming, their windows curtained with muslin or lace, their chimneys pouring out the smoke of burning wood, looked as friendly as the word welcome. As for the Raleigh Tavern, it translated hospitality into beauty and form. The broad, low steps, narrowing slightly as they marched to the cupola-crowned platform before the paneled door of dark polished wood which centered the front of the building, seemed to beg you to enter. The house was wide and low, of wood painted white, and had three exquisitely proportioned windows on either side of the entrance, each window with its wide-flung wooden shutters, dark and polished like the door. From the slightly projecting eave the roof climbed steeply to the ridge that carried two stout brick chimneys, a row of seven dormer windows with peaked gables projecting boldly from the slope, to beam pleasantly down on all who entered, through their looped mull curtains. Tall trees stood to either side, and in front, beyond the brick pavement that had been laid by the owners of the inn, was a long row of posts and heavy rails to which riders hitched their steeds before entering, a couple of Negro boys standing by to give what assistance might be demanded. Firmly planted beside the central opening in this row was a tall, white standard from which depended the large, heavily-framed portrait of the Elizabethan hero for whom the tavern was named.

In the near future this hostelry would be the scene of history-making meetings, but as yet it was no more than the center of gaiety, excellent food, and noble wines it was built to be.

As the three men entered, a burst of laughter and talk came from the tap-room, opening out of the small reception-room to the left of the entrance. Some one in the crowd before the bar caught sight of Henry and came quickly toward him. It was John Fleming, from Cumberland, who had supported Henry in the resolutions against the Stamp Act. Greeting the three, Fleming asked them to eat with a small group in one of the side rooms, men who wanted to meet Henry, and were with him in the popular stand against further infringements of liberty in America by the British government.

It was to be the first of many such meetings, and Patrick was to feel, before he left to begin his ride home, that the patriot party in Virginia was alert and daring. The consensus of opinion boiled down to the fact that the future hung on whether or not Britain would repeal the one remaining tax, and admit she had no power to impose any tax on the colonies. If she made this admission and stuck to it, well and good. If not ...

If not?

The group turned their eyes on Henry, who glanced from one to the other, a faint smile on his lips. He had been sitting slumped back in his chair, his fingers lightly tapping the polished wooden arms. Now he straightened, lifting his head and letting his gaze rest on the leaping flames of the fire on the hearth opposite:

"Why, in that case, gentlemen, we shall learn what price we must pay to remain free men."

On that, almost as though it had been a signal, the tableful arose and began to disperse. Soon after, in his riding clothes and with his saddle-bags slung over his horse, Patrick was on his way back to Hanover.

Some weeks passed before the news spread through the colonies that the royal officers in Massachusetts had been ordered to collect evidence against certain suspected men of influence with the view of arresting them and deporting them to England for trial. Implicit in the order was the threat to any other Assembly which should support Massachusetts, or any man in the colonies whose actions could be construed as treasonable to Great Britain.

A great upswing of anger and of alarm swept Virginia. Here was something far worse, far more dangerous, than the imposing of a tax. Here was an attack on personal liberty. The election of new members to the Assembly showed the rapid rise of a patriot spirit, almost every man being a strong believer in resistance by all possible means, as the campaign speeches made clear.

Patrick Henry would now represent Hanover. And among the new members was the name of Thomas Jefferson.

The Governor called the Assembly to meet May 11, 1769. Well before the day set most of the Burgesses had reached Williamsburg, with them Henry. There would thus be time for discussion among the delegates, before the session opened.

Chapter 8

BLAZING THE WAY, BY RESOLUTIONS TO RESOLUTION

THE Assembly convened on May 11th in a spirit of subdued excitement and was addressed by Governor Botetourt in words revealing his real affection for the Colony, yet at the same time his lack of understanding as to the temper of the men to whom he spoke. After remarking on the King's high regard toward Virginia, witnessed by the fact that he had himself been appointed its governor and not its deputy governor, as heretofore, with the assurance that this would hold in all future appointments, he added that his heart and soul were devoted to the Virginians, and that he would do all in his power, even to the risk of life and fortune, to further their interests.

He mentioned that he had taken the advice of the Council in declaring the writs of assistance illegal [these writs were the warrants to customs officers to enter and search any premises at pleasure] and he ended by asking the Assembly to pass no resolutions sustaining Massachusetts. He sat down to applause and was answered and thanked for what he had done in a manner that showed the Virginians liked and approved of him.

That night the Governor wrote a confident letter to the Secretary of the Colonies in England assuring that gentleman that he was certain the Assembly had come together in a spirit of good humor and harmony toward the Ministry.

Poor man, he little knew his Assembly!

For no sooner had the Governor departed than the House got down to what really mattered. First came the reading of the Joint Address of the Lords and Commons to the King, directly attacking the rights of person and of jury trial in the colonies. It roused considerable anger, and was the earliest direct report of the matter to be brought before the people's representatives, some of whom had not even heard of this threat to Massachusetts, for news traveled slowly, and the Governor of Massachusetts had made no attempt to hasten its pace. A number of the Burgesses who had been but half-hearted in the matter of supporting Massachusetts in the tax bill controversy, joined the whole of heart immediately. One after another men spoke for upholding the northern colony against Parliament's attack. Richard Henry Lee read a passage from a letter written him several months earlier by John Dickinson running to this effect:

"Virginia, Sir, has maintained the common cause with such attention, spirit and temper as has gained her the highest degree of reputation among the other colonies. It is as much in her power to dishearten them, as to encourage them."

Dickinson was the Pennsylvanian author of "The Farmer" articles.

It was agreed that whatever business must be attended to by the Burgesses should be finished before any resolutions in regard to Virginia's attitude were reported. Also that proceedings regarding them should be held behind closed doors, as it was felt certain the Governor would dissolve the Assembly before it had completed its work if he got wind of what was toward.

Most of the business concerned the forming of committees. Henry was appointed on a number of them, including the important Privileges and Elections, Propositions and Grievances, and Religion. When these met, Henry always acted as Chairman, and was to serve on them regularly in the future.

Then, May 16th, five days after the House had met, the Committee of the Whole reported the following resolutions. Their bold directness of speech spoke Patrick Henry's hand, and it was also believed that he wrote the Address to the King, which followed. Here are the Resolutions, four in number:

Resolved, without opposition (Nemine contradicente), That the sole right of imposing taxes on this, his Majesty's colony and dominion of Virginia, is now and ever has been, legally and constitutionally vested in the House of Burgesses, legally convened, according to the ancient and established practice, with the consent of the Council, and of his Majesty the King of England, or his Governor for the time being.

Resolved, etc. That it is the undoubted privilege of the inhabitants of this colony to petition their sovereign for the redress of grievances and that it is lawful and expedient to procure the concurrence of his Majesty's other colonies, in dutiful addresses praying the royal interposition in favor of the violated rights of America.

Resolved, etc., That all trials of treason, misprision of treason, or of any other felony or crime whatsoever, committed or done in his Majesty's said colony and dominion, by any person or persons residing therein, ought of right to be conducted in and before his Majesty's courts held within his said colony, according to the fixed and known course of proceeding. And that the seizing of any person or persons residing in this colony, suspected of any crime whatsoever committed therein, and sending such person or persons beyond the sea to be tried, is highly derogatory of the rights of British subjects, as thereby the inestimable privilege of being tried by a jury from their vicinage, as well as the liberty of summoning and procuring witnesses in such a trial, will be taken away from the party accused.

Resolved, etc., That an humble, dutiful and loyal address be presented to his Majesty to assure him of our inviolable attachment to his sacred person and government, and to beseech his royal intervention as the father of his people, however remote from the seat of his empire, to quiet the minds of his loyal subjects of this colony, and to avert from them those dangers and miseries which will ensue from the seizing and carrying beyond sea any person residing in America suspected of any crime whatsoever, to be tried in any other manner than by the ancient and long-established course of proceeding.

Copies of the above resolves were sent to the Speakers of every Assembly, and in addition, reported and agreed to by the House, they were ordered published in the *Virginia Gazette.* John Blair, President of the Council, Robert Henry Lee, R. C. Nicholas, Thomas Mason, Benjamin Harrison, and Patrick Henry were appointed to draw up the Address to the King, which they turned in next day. All of this, with the orders to print, were finished and done with before the Burgesses were summoned to attend the

Governor. This they did cheerfully. He made them the briefest of speeches, and he made it sadly:

"Mr. Speaker and Gentlemen of the House of Representatives, I have heard of your resolves, and augur ill of their effects; you have made it my duty to dissolve you, and you are accordingly dissolved."

Simple as good-by.

The Burgesses adjourned, to meet in the beautiful Apollo Room of the Raleigh, long and admirably proportioned, with a wide, generous hearth and damask-curtained windows. Here they signed an *Agreement* presented by George Washington and drawn up by George Mason, who was not at that time in public life but earnestly interested in the serious task of opposing Parliament. This agreement pledged each man in his particular section of the colony to encourage frugality, industry, and a firm refusal to buy any articles taxed by Parliament. Several colonies had preceded Virginia in such an agreement and before long all had joined in it. That done, the Burgesses departed for their own homes. There was plenty to do in forming and strengthening public opinion.

While this was going on in America, Parliament was having a tough time in England. A strong, cleverly-led minority in Parliament was resisting every step in the Ministry's oppression of the colonies. Edmund Burke was the powerful leader in this movement, whose every speech in Commons underlined and condemned the tyrannical behavior of the two houses. Following his suggestions a party was formed among the people in general, who saw the danger to trade in the new non-importation agreement, sure to have bitter results for the manufacturers and traders. Another situation developed when the *Letters of Junius* were published, brutal and scathing personal attacks on the King and several of his ministers, which did not tend to make life easier for them; especially Junius fought for the return to Parliament of Pitt, the Earl of Chatham, who had recovered his health and was known as a stout champion of America.

From Virginia, in addition, came letters written by Governor Botetourt doing his best to help his colony, imploring the ministers to cease their injustice to a people he declared to be loyal and patriotic, but not submissive to tyranny in whatever form.

All of this forced Parliament to kill the whole tax bill except for the one item insisted upon by the King—tea. The Governor of each colony was told to inform his Assembly of the repeal, to be in force as soon as the Parliament met again; but they were also ordered to explain that the move was made "upon consideration of such duties having been laid contrary to the true principles of commerce." Up to this time the duties had merely been remitted, Massachusetts alone excepted, not repealed. As for the trial in England of so-called treasonable men, that appeared to have fizzled out through sheer inability to lay hands on any such persons.

When the Assembly met again the following November, Botetourt addressed the members in the name of the British Ministry, proclaiming the decision reached by Parliament, and giving them his word that there would be no further attempt to raise revenues in America.

Tea was not much drunk in Virginia, which had its coffee and liked it, and beyond an expression by the Council to the effect that Parliament must repeal all taxes, the question was dropped. The House of Burgesses took pains to let the Governor know how highly he was appreciated by his people, telling him that his constant efforts to help them had made him truly beloved.

This was true. The honest, kind, and lovable character of the little man had brought him a lasting affection which revealed itself after his death, less than a year later, in the statue raised to his memory, that stands to-day before the main building of the college, to which he had given much.

The only remaining business of a serious nature was in regard to the Indians. Patrick Henry was placed at the head of the Committee on Indian Affairs. Its work had two aims; one to see that certain men who had murdered a number of friendly Indians in order to grab their lands should be brought to justice, the second and more important to establish a broad view of the whole Indian question, and to make it illegal for any one to make any sort of treaty with them, or to enter into negotiations for buying land from them. The Government alone was to have these rights. It was an important decision, valuable to the Colony later on, when Virginia maintained it against the claims of individuals and especially of land companies claiming to own great tracts of her western territory by such private treaties. As for the criminals, who had already once before been thrown into prison, only to be rescued by their friends, they finally left the Colony either by way of the hangman's noose or by escaping southward beyond the border.

Another important matter allied to the above was the line marking the western boundary between the Colony and the Indians. The Board of Trade had proposed a line starting from the extension of North Carolina at the point where it touched the Holston River and so on to the mouth of the Kanawa where it joins the Ohio. This line would not only have cut off some of Virginia's settlements, but would have left to the Indians all of what one day was to be Kentucky, as well as a goodly piece of to-day's West Virginia; also it would have increased the danger of attack from hostile tribes. Henry persuaded his committee to insist on another line to start at the northwestern corner of North Carolina and so continue straight west to the Ohio. This included Kentucky, much of which was held by the Cherokees. All land so held was to be purchased by the Colony and then the land sold in reasonable quantities and as cheaply as possible to prospective settlers, excluding all monopolies.

Patrick's desire, being always for the individual and the poor man, was to stop the threat of such companies as those already trying to grab vast areas to be developed to their own profit, and also to encourage western emigration by citizens of the colony or new immigrants seeking homes. He was successful in getting these two plans, to acquire the land and to help the settlers, adopted, but it took time and steady work. Lord Hillsborough in England was dead against the whole idea. He wanted the population kept close to the seaboard, where it would be a lot easier to control, and where it would be more profitable for the British trade.

The Four Resolutions, as well as the Address to the King, which drew his Majesty's attention to the situation while also assuring him of the love and loyalty of his Virginian subjects, met high approval from colony after colony as the different Assemblies met. Several adopted them verbatim; others rewrote them to suit themselves, but held to what they stood for. Everywhere men breathed a freer air.

It had been a crowded year for Patrick. Settling his

family in the new home he had chosen not far from Mount Brilliant, attending the two sessions of the Assembly, and furthermore appearing at the Bar of the General Court in Williamsburg, where he met and more than held his own with all the top men of his profession, kept him at the height of his energy. He loved it. Nor did he fail to enjoy an inner amusement at the very evident amazement of many at the General Court to find he knew his law. Here were Pendleton, Wythe, John Randolph, Nicholas, several more of the great. Judge Winston, who read law with him, admitted Henry's skill was astonishing. The rest had spent their lives since boyhood reading law under the leading teachers. "How," remarks Winston, "was it possible that in reasoning with any man on general principles he did not lose in comparison with such competitors? Yet I never heard that he betrayed the least lack of legal knowledge. To me it has always seemed that without much labor he acquired information which others only got through painful research."

This conclusion sounds reasonable!

In fact, it looks as though Henry were the cleverer, the quicker, that he did not need to sweat over what he studied, to go over and over what he read. It was his at one reading. There could be no other explanation, but how some of his colleagues hated to admit it! Henry had his specialty, suited to his genius, preferring jury trials, where he could work on the human element, and he was especially interested in criminal cases; also especially popular, for those he consented to take, he won. Yet he handled other cases with the same ease and skill as any among the best, cases in which his eloquence had nothing to do. Not but that he could combine sound argument with eloquence, as he showed this very first year, when he appeared as counsel for the captain of a Spanish vessel that, together with its cargo, had been libeled under the oppressive Navigation Act. William Nelson, who was a member of the court, declared:

"I never heard a more argumentative yet at the same time more eloquent speech than the one Henry made. He was immeasurably superior to either Mason or Pendleton, who both argued in the same cause. What's more I was astonished at the familiarity he showed with maritime law to which, to the best of my belief, he had never, till then, paid the least attention."

Patrick had a gracious and charming bearing when appearing as counsel before the Bar, modest, mild, sometimes almost shy. Tall, slender, slightly stooped at shoulder, dressed in black with a tie wig, his face thin with high cheekbones and a nose of the Roman type, speaking in a voice of a telling quality but never harsh even when raised under stress of emotion, he had a smile, as St. George Tucker put it, in which you might "anticipate a certain want of conviction" even at the moment he "submitted to the 'superior wisdom' of the court with a grace that would have done honor to the most polished courtier in Westminster Hall." Henry's expression while arguing a case was always grave, even when he roused a laugh by some neat turn or flash of wit, and he showed his excitement in an argument more often by what came to be called the "Patrick flash" of those deep-set blue eyes than by tone of voice or facial expression. Only at times of great emotion and in a high patriotic cause would he tower, lift his arms in a magnificent movement, and let his feeling charge his voice.

Between times, at home, Henry attended to his own law cases, looked about for an estate that would suit his needs, and hunted. But time for hunting was rare now, and would almost disappear in the following, ever-heightening days leading toward revolution. So far no one had thought of that possibility. Botetourt, who had continued his efforts with the Ministry, was confident at the time he called the next Assembly meeting, in May, 1770, that his pleas had been regarded, and that all and every attempt to lay a tax on the colonies was over.

Chapter 9

ENTER THE LAST ROYAL GOVERNOR

IT was not until April, 1770, that the Act abolishing
all taxes but that on tea finally passed in Parliament.
Botetourt called the Assembly to meet in May, and on
June 20th the Governor reported to the House of Burgesses, telling them he bitterly felt that his promise to
them, a promise he had thought securely based on fact,
that all taxes were to be repealed and the taxing of the
colonies by Britain ended, had not been kept. The blow
was so hard that it affected his already failing health,
bringing on his death in October, after weeks in bed.

As for the Assembly, they were thoroughly disgusted.
Most of them had felt certain the King would listen to
their Governor's earnest request, and here they were, back

at the starting point! The House ordered, as soon as the Governor had returned to the Palace, that a petition to the King be drawn up next day. Patrick was always called on on these occasions, and the following paragraph carries his hall mark: That the King "recommend to his parliament a total repeal of certain Acts lately passed for the purpose of raising a revenue in America, and for subjecting American property to the jurisdiction of distant and arbitrary courts of admiralty, where trial by jury is not permitted, and where distance and ignorance may both conspire to ruin the innocent."

Henry, intensely occupied on different committees, was busier still when the Assembly adjourned in organizing committees in his own county to carry out the plans made before the adjournment by the members, who had created a new association pledged to see that the decisions reached were carried out all over the country: no taxed articles to be bought, the agreement on non-importation strictly enforced, the use of tea entirely ended.

In this year Patrick's father completed his extensive and detailed map of Virginia, which he sent to England to be published. This took a deal of money, so much that the old man sold his rights in it to Patrick. Copies arrived in Virginia some weeks after publication, and one at least existed in Warrenton not many years ago. It is a thing any lover of the state would like to see published to-day. John Henry's work on it was a true love-labor, and those friends of his who saw it spoke words of admiration and astonishment, for it was not only a map, but, with its comments, a story.

This year, in July, Henry journeyed all the way to New York, his first travel beyond his own colony. He had been commissioned, with other commissioners from Quebec,

New York, New Jersey, Maryland, Pennsylvania, and Delaware, to meet in New York City to work out a general plan, suggested by himself, to regulate the Indian trade, a valuable trade although utterly haphazard and unorganized. But when the delegates arrived, like the King of France and his twenty thousand men, they had to turn and ride back again. The Governor forbade the meeting; he feared it would prove a strong step forward in the determined move to unite the different colonies, and he advised other royal governors to oppose it.

You get a pretty clear idea of a country when you ride through it on a horse, and Henry immensely enjoyed his journey. New York still looked a lot like New Amsterdam, and decidedly unlike Williamsburg, and Philadelphia was unlike either. Too, there were the people, the townsfolk, the farmer folk with whom he stayed overnight, the travelers along the roads he passed over. He would draw them into talk with his delightful skill in leading men on to express themselves, putting seeming-idle queries that set a fellow yarning as though the stranger were an old friend.

It wasn't wasted, that long ride, even though failing in the reason which got it going. When Patrick reached Hanover County and his own home he very likely knew more of the general mood and outlook of the people along that stretch of our country than any dozen habitual travelers would ever have.

When Governor Botetourt died in October, William Nelson, President of the Council, as was customary, took over. A county had been named after Botetourt, and here, along the upper section of the James River, Patrick bought a fine tract of land. It was another investment for the future. His two older sons, John and William, were now going to school and no longer ran yelling and barefoot over the land. They were dressed as well as any other among the boys of the neighborhood, and seemed to learn fast enough not to be long at the foot of their class. When Patrick was home and not too busy he would still go a-hunting, taking John with him, the boy already being an expert shot. All the children were developed in thought and speech beyond their ages, constant playing and talking with their father having been as good, or perhaps much better, an education than the little country school could have provided. Especially as Henry talked to his sons and daughters as to equals. They heard his stories of Williamsburg, of the British attempt to crush the spirit of freedom in Virginia, and friends dropping in of an evening would often find him with one of his little girls in his lap, the rest of the children crowded about him, Sarah with some piece of sewing in her hands seated near. The family was happy, but besides that, it was cheerful.

In his talks with his children Patrick used the same careless manner that he had with adults whose opinions and desires he wished to learn. There was never a taint of heavy father about him. When he came home from Williamsburg or from one of his rounds to his neighboring courts, there was always a rush of young feet hurrying toward him. At home his face lost the gravity it had in the Assembly or the General Court. He was easy to be with, always, but he was more so at home than even with his friends, charming as he was with them. And he was dramatic to his family, too, when drama was called for in some tale he was telling. Another thing he loved to do was to ride over to Mount Brilliant for midday dinner with his father and mother. And the old man's excitement when his map was at last really in his hands was shared by his son. The two pored over it together while the Colonel

pointed out this or the other item which had been particularly difficult.

"We had fairly definite boundaries to the counties, but
some of these rivers were a task. Of course there are errors,
but take it all together it's nothing to be ashamed of," the
father said, with the under-statement habitual to him,
although he was secretly bursting with pride. Here was
the first map of the colony he loved, and he'd made it.

"Ashamed of!" quizzed Patrick. "It's beautiful and you
know it. I'll take a copy with me when I go back to the
capital and make the Assembly ashamed of not paying for
it themselves. Father, this is a land worth keeping free. On
my journey to New York I felt it as I had not yet. Good
land, good people, people who have changed the wilderness to farms and towns, who, as Scripture says, have made
it flow with milk and honey. Our land, Father. And with
all the strength in me I'm going to fight to keep us free
men. No matter how far that determination leads us."

The two exchanged glances, and the Colonel nodded
his head slowly. "Yes, Pat, I understand. And you're right.
No matter how far."

In July, 1771, President of the Council and Governor
pro tem, Mr. William Nelson, called the Assembly to meet.
Little was done beyond voting assistance to sufferers from
severe freshets which, in May, had swept away much of
the tobacco stored in the public sheds along the shore of
Chesapeake Bay, where the people owning the small farms
kept it, like money in a bank. The General Court held its
sessions, too, which Henry attended, dressed in black velvet
or silk, with a powdered wig, having rounded curls laid
over the temples, the custom among the lawyers at that
Court. And when the weather was chill he threw a long

scarlet cloak over his shoulders. But when making his rounds back home he wore a plain suit of black cloth with a dark tie wig. At the Assembly meetings he could be seen in a peach-colored silk coat. Always now he wore a high white stock and ruffles.

During 1771 Mr. Henry bought a fine estate known as Scotchtown into which he moved his family. He had been seeking what he wanted for some time, and paid six hundred pounds, a large price, but was congratulated by his friends on a good bargain. Brother-in-law William Christian wrote him that he couldn't have found a better place, and was also able to tell him that the lands he had bought on the James suffered not at all from the floods. In fact, Henry was making good money at his profession, and handling his money wisely.

In the autumn the new governor arrived, a Scot, John Murray, Earl of Dunmore. He had been in New York, where he was heartily disliked, and after meeting him Edmund Randolph described him in these high-flown but telling words:

To external accomplishments he pretended not, and his manners and sentiments did not surpass substantial barbarism; a barbarism which was not palliated by a particle of native genius, nor regulated by any ingredient of religion. His propensities were coarse and depraved.

A striking contrast, this, to the gentle and polished Governor whom he followed. Virginia hated and despised him from the first.

Lord Dunmore called the Assembly to meet in February, 1772, but nothing much happened except that Henry pushed for an appeal to the King to put an end to the slave trade. The outcome was an Address to the King, probably written by Henry, strongly protesting against the continuance of this traffic. The Colony was not permitted to put an end to it, nor even to impose duties that would help check these importations of wild African Negroes, which threatened to swamp the country. For a number of years Virginia had been trying to get the King to assent to this restraining measure, but in vain, because his Majesty got a percentage for each black dumped on the colonies. Already the proportion of Negro to White was close upon ten to eleven. The Assembly, in the Address, now warned the King that the trade threatened to "endanger the very existence of the colonies," adding that it was an "inhuman and pernicious commerce."

In January of the next year Henry wrote to thank a friend who had sent him a book famous at that time, written by a Frenchman, Antoine Benezet, on slavery. It is worth reading, this letter, as it gives a clear notion of Patrick's horror of slavery, and yet indicates the impossibility of getting along without slaves in those times and circumstances.

Dear Sir... Is it not amazing that at a time when the rights of humanity are understood and defined with precision, in a country above all others fond of liberty, that in such an age, and in such a country we find men professing a religion the most humane, gentle and generous, adopting a principle as repugnant to humanity as it is inconsistent with the Bible, and destructive to liberty? Every thinking, honest man rejects it in speculation—how few in practice...

Would any one believe I am master of slaves of my own purchase! I am drawn along by the general inconvenience of living here without them. I will not, I cannot justify it...

I believe a time will come when an opportunity will be offered to abolish this lamentable evil. Everything we can do is to improve it, if it happens in our day. If not, let us transmit to our descendants, together with our slaves, a pity for their unhappy lot and an abhorrence of slavery... I could say many things on this subject, a serious view of which gives a gloomy perspective to future times.

No man ever spoke more truly! The next century was to prove it, and even to-day the South still pays a heavy price for that long-past iniquity.

Henry made another prophetic announcement a little later. He, with Colonel John Overton, and two others, Colonel Morris and Mr. John Hawkins, were together at the home of Overton's brother Samuel discussing the increasing stress of events when Samuel turned to Patrick and asked:

"Do you suppose, Mr. Henry, that Great Britain will drive her colonies to extremities? Suppose we are driven to war, what would be the outcome?"

Henry glanced about the room to make sure who was present before he answered.

"She *will* drive us to extremities—no accommodation will occur—hostilities are sure to commence, and a desperate and bloody touch it will be."

"But then," Samuel Overton continued, "do you think an infant nation as we are, without discipline, arms, ammunition, ships of war, or money to procure them—do you think it possible, thus circumstanced, successfully to oppose the fleets and armies of Great Britain?"

"I will be candid with you. I doubt whether we shall be able, *alone,* to cope with so powerful a nation, but—" and with a smooth and supple motion, characteristic both of his mind and his body, Patrick was on his feet, his eyes ablaze with animation, "but where is France? Where is Spain? Where is Holland? The natural enemies of Great Britain—where will they be all this time? Do you suppose they will stand by, idle and indifferent spectators to the contest? Will Louis XVI be asleep all the time? Believe me, *no!* When Louis XVI shall be satisfied, by our serious opposition and our *declaration of independence,* that all prospect of reconciliation is gone, then, and not till then, will he furnish us with arms, ammunition, clothing; and not with these only, but he will send his fleets and armies to help fight our battles; he will form with us a treaty offensive and defensive against our unnatural mother. Spain and Holland will join the confederation! Our independence will be established, and we shall take our place among the nations of the earth!"

He sat down.

At the word *independence* the company had glanced at each other with startled eyes. Never had they heard anything of that kind so much as suggested until then. And when, later, Colonel Overton spoke of this evening he said that never while he lived could he forget the tone of Patrick's voice nor the manner in which the prophecy was given.

The little company separated soon after, almost in silence. They had been given stuff to think about. Independence. A great word, a word to ponder over—a magnificent word.

Chapter 10

BEACONS OF MOUNTING STORM

SOMETHING had happened in the harbor of Providence, Rhode Island, in June of 1772, which was to have strong repercussions not alone in that colony but in the others, including Virginia. It emphasized the truth of Patrick Henry's conviction that Britain would continue to oppress her colonies until they were driven to fight.

An English ship of war, the *Gaspée*, commanded by Lieutenant Dudington, had been busy for months intercepting commerce by stopping and searching colonial vessels using Newport Harbor, and when she felt like it seizing their cargoes. This was entirely without any lawful right, and the people of that section were growing very tired of it. So when on June 9th the *Gaspée* ran herself aground chasing a Providence packet, a number of men wearing masks and using muffled oars, rowed to the stranded ship, climbed aboard before the crew was aware, had a sharp scuffle when the men waked up to what was going on, wounding the lieutenant before mastering the rest and tying them up. The attackers loaded their captives into the rowboats, lighted fires throughout the ship, slipped off, and landed the officer and his men on shore, releasing one or two who could unbind the rest. Not a word had been spoken by the colonists throughout the adventure, although a few chuckles had been heard as they trussed up the crew. The job finished, they slipped quietly away in the darkness, not a single man among them recognized either by the crew of the *Gaspée*, who had naturally been ashore a good bit, or any King's men living in Providence.

The *Gaspée* was a complete loss, and the Royal Governors of Rhode Island, New Jersey, New York, and Massachusetts, for the warship had been raiding in all these harbors, were in a complete fury, agreeing inconsistently that this sort of thing simply wasn't done, but that those who did it should be arrested and hauled in irons to England to be tried. However, no one offered himself for trial, nor had any living soul, so far as might be discovered, the faintest notion who could possibly have been involved. In our day the Gremlins would be blamed and the matter forgotten, but not then. In January, 1773, the Governors appointed the Chief Justices of their several colonies to meet with the Vice-Admiralty Judge, to proceed with the arrest of the criminals and then get them to England. For the whole of the following year these worthy gentlemen were to talk to each other, to come and go, to make not a single arrest, and finally to separate and return to their particular jobs with only a long report to show for their pains, most of it given over to a not entirely successful effort to explain away the illegal conduct of Lieutenant Dudington. Nevertheless, they had accomplished something else. They had been an important item in drawing the colonies closer together, and in stiffening the spirit of resistance among the people.

When the news of this first meeting of Justices reached Virginia, Patrick Henry left his home, Scotchtown, for Williamsburg. He wanted to talk with leading men there concerning the importance of inducing the colonies to act together against the increasing tyranny of Parliament, to create some sort of union that would have tangible results. It was known that the Assembly was to be called soon, probably by March 1st. Lord Dunmore had been proroguing it steadily since his advent, but a large number of forged bank notes had come into circulation, there was danger of a financial panic, and the Burgesses must meet to handle the affair.

It wasn't of bank notes that the select company who presently met in a private room of the Raleigh Tavern talked, however. It was of this vital need for united action. Jefferson makes a note of this meeting as follows:

Not thinking our old and leading members up to the point of forwardness and zeal which the times required, Mr. Henry, Richard Henry Lee, Francis L. Lee, Mr. Carr and myself agreed to meet in the evening . . . to consider the British claims as a common cause to all, and to produce a unity of action; and for this purpose that a committee of correspondence in each colony would be the best means of intercommunication; and that the first measure would probably be to propose a meeting of deputies from every colony at some central place, who would be charged with the direction of the measures which should be taken by all.

Henry was still busy with meetings and discussions when, early in February, news was brought to him that his father had died. He left at once for Mount Brilliant. It was sorrow to the son, and also an unexpected blow, for his father had apparently been in good health when Patrick left home. Colonel John was not yet seventy, a man of a gentle and quiet spirit and sound body who should have had several years before him. But he had slipped into death as gently and quietly as he had lived. Coming to Virginia an immigrant, with little money, he had served his adopted country as Judge and Colonel, had left a family behind him well provided for, all his six daughters married to excellent men, some of whom became important in the history of the Revolution to come, his elder son with an excellent farm and a good wife, and his second son, Patrick, one of the leading men of the Colony and head of the Assembly, of whom George Mason, another great Virginian, was to say in the following year, "He is, in my opinion, the first man upon this continent, as well in abilities as public virtue."

For a time at least it was agreed that the widow should stay on at the family home. One of her daughters brought her two small children and came to be with her until decisions could be reached. Patrick, too, stayed on for a while, attending to some law business waiting for him, visiting his own family at Scotchtown, and planning some changes in his new home.

Scotchtown was built by a Scot, Colonel Chiswell, who had bought a thousand acres of rich land as a proper frame for his noble Hall, set facing south on a flat-topped hill with a fine outlook on every side. The wide south porch had a particularly lovely view over a sweep of cultivated land and fields, bordered by forest. A broad flight of stone

steps led down into these fields, and several great trees
stood within shade's reach of the whole façade, a pleasant
thing on summer days. There was a second porch on this
same side, somewhat smaller, and each had a shapely
gabled roof supported by pillars.

The building was a story-and-a-half high, the roof
slightly hipped at either end, giving the upper floor considerable room. Gable windows looked out from the roof,
and below these the long windows of the main floor let in
plenty of light to each of the eight rooms that stretched
from end to end of the long building. These rooms all
opened through doorways on the north side into a handsome hall with its own row of windows. The porches were
reached through fine colonial doorways from the two main
rooms, the dining hall and the living room, as we would
call it to-day. Stairs at one end of the hallway led up to
the great garret, large enough, people said, to accommodate every dancer in Hanover if the Colonel should give
them a party. It was this garret that Patrick was planning
to finish with several bedrooms where he could put guests.
There was a basement, which had a small dungeon in one
end, probably used by the Scot to punish bad slaves.

Inside as out, Scotchtown was a house of noble proportions and charming appearance. The walls of the long hall
and the two main rooms were paneled with walnut. Each
room had its large corner fireplace of black marble with
white, fluted marble columns supporting the mantelshelf.
Above the roof four tall brick chimneys rose, two at either
end. And behind, side by side, fronting on a brick path,
ran the service buildings, ending in the stables and a
windmill, all built of brick from England.

Chiswell had been a fiery-tempered but delightful man,
fond of a good game of cards, and a glass of wine, never

missing the Season at Williamsburg, to which he drove in his fine coach drawn by a pair of spirited horses by way of Negro-foot Road past his gates and so along the highway. His fierceness and his love of cards led to his end. In a quarrel breaking between himself and another player the Colonel somehow ran his sword through the other chap, killing him then and there. Which brash act brought him to the handsome little prison of the Capital, where presently he died. And it was from his estate that Patrick bought the place.

It lay in that part of Hanover County where Henry had spent his childhood, a few miles from the junction of the North and South Anna Rivers, where the Forks Church stood, the Presbyterian Church he had often attended with his mother after she joined that faith, an experience that helped to make him so unbigoted in religion.

A gruesome occurrence had given Negro-foot Road its name. Long before Henry's day, on a farm some two or three miles nearer the highway, a slave freshly arrived from Africa showed an extreme fondness for a toddling Negro orphan, took him into his own hut, petted him, fed him, watching over him carefully until the little fellow was a perfect chunk of fat. And then the child disappeared.

Inquiry followed, resulting in a cannibal story, the only one Virginia ever had. The cannibal's master killed the man and cut off one foot, which he nailed to a stake driven into the ground beside the road, near where the Negro's cabin had stood. The cabin was burnt down, and in time the foot disintegrated; but the name clung to the road through the generations. Patrick had often trudged along Negro-foot Road in his boyhood, and now he owned the great estate alongside which it ran. He remembered, with a sympathetic grin, how scared he had been in those past days if he had had to walk that way after sundown.

In addition to these different activities Patrick took time to call on his neighbors, among others the Dandridges, and to get their opinions on what the future might bring. He believed entirely, as he was to tell the group of his friends later in Williamsburg, that war was the certain outcome, but of this he did not speak. As always, it was the other man's opinion he sought. Most of them were angry at the way Britain was acting, but seemed not yet aware that what touched Rhode Island and Massachusetts, touched them, too. Dandridge was the exception, and confided to Patrick that he would not be surprised if the colonies broke with England.

"But I still think that the King will see reason and let us be. It is stupid obstinacy to keep nagging at us; surely the Ministry will see this truth, and they may be able to persuade his Royal Majesty of the grim results of continuing this useless conduct. One can but hope."

"Hope is a pleasant indulgence, Mr. Dandridge, and can do no harm. But neither can it be of any real help. And as for me, I have little faith that the King will see reason. Some will have it he is mad; I cannot say, but I do say that he acts like a madman."

March came and Henry was back in Williamsburg. The first thing before the House was the bank-bill forgery. Before the meeting Governor Dunmore had arrested a number of suspects in Pittsylvania, ordering them to be tried without first being brought, according to law, before an examining court. He now sent a message to the Assembly with the information that one of their own members, Paschal Greenhill, had been accused under oath of passing several counterfeit bills. Greenhill was still at large and the Governor demanded his instant arrest, with action against the other accused men.

Patrick Henry was named chairman of a committee appointed to wait on the Governor with the answer of the House. This answer took the form of a resolve, probably Henry's work, since he was made chairman. It thanked his Excellency for the information in regard to Mr. Greenhill, as "an instance of his Lordship's tenderness and affection for the privileges of the members of this House," a neat backhanded compliment, assured him that the House was "filled with a just detestation of an offense so dangerous in its consequences," and entreated his Lordship to direct that "every legal step be taken" in order that Mr. Greenhill as well as the others accused might be brought to justice. It also engaged its word that it would cheerfully pay "any reasonable reward his Excellency may think fit to offer for apprehending such offenders, to be paid upon their conviction."

All of which was a nudge in his Excellency's ribs to stop acting without due observance of the rules.

The Governor was asked at the same time to lay before the House the proceedings in the case of the supposed criminals. When these arrived the Assembly passed an Address to his Lordship, but decided not to present it until it had finished all the business before it, knowing very well that it would then be dismissed at once.

The business consisted of passing the required legislation for calling in the forged money and for punishing the men convicted of the forgery. The Assembly also agreed on the steps necessary for the work needed to improve navigation on the Potomac, for the making of new roads and the building of a canal around the falls of the James and York rivers. Then with the coming of March 12th (they had met on the 4th) the real work and great reason of their meeting was taken up; this was the inauguration of standing committees of correspondence and inquiry, whose initial inspiration was that of the younger members in the meeting at the Raleigh Tavern already mentioned.

These resolutions, drawn up on March 12, 1773, marked the first conception of the United States of America. Here was union against tyranny, and for freedom. Here were words as plainly to be understood as yea and nay. Let us read them.

Whereas the minds of his Majesty's faithful subjects in the colony have been much disturbed by various rumors and reports of proceedings tending to deprive them of their ancient, legal and constitutional rights,

And Whereas, the affairs of this colony are frequently connected with those of Great Britain, as well as those of the neighboring colonies, which renders a communication of sentiments necessary; in order therefore to remove the uneasiness and quiet the minds of the people, as well as for the other good purposes above mentioned,

Be it resolved, That a standing committee of correspondence and inquiry be appointed to consist of 11 persons, to wit: The honorable Peyton Randolph, Robert Carter Nicholas, Richard Bland, Henry Lee, Benjamin Harrison, Edmund Pendleton, Patrick Henry, Dudley Diggs, Archibald Cary and Thomas Jefferson, Esquires; and six of whom to be a committee, whose business it shall be to obtain the most early and authentic intelligence of all such acts and resolutions of the British Parliament, or proceedings of Administration, as may relate to or affect the British Colonies in America, and to keep up and maintain a correspondence with our sister colonies, respecting those important considerations; and the result of such their proceedings, from time to time, to lay before the House.

Resolved, That it be an instruction to the said committee, that they do without delay inform themselves particularly of the principles and authority on which was constituted a court of inquiry, said to have been lately held in Rhode Island, with power to transmit persons accused of committing offences here in America, to places beyond the seas to be tried.

Henry made a splendid speech for the adoption of the resolves, and was followed next day by Richard Henry Lee. No transcript remains of either talk, nor even any résumé. But there is an interesting item communicated by young St. George Tucker. Tucker had not heard Henry yet, except for brief remarks concerned with the business before the House, but he had heard Lee, and admired him tremendously. As Lee was to speak on the same subject the day following Henry's talk, and Tucker could not get away for both speeches, he chose Lee. "Never before," he says, "had I heard what I thought oratory." He said as much to a couple of his fellow collegians, who had heard both men.

They told him that Lee was good, of course, but nothing beside Henry. "If his [Lee's] speech was excelled by Mr. Henry's the latter must have been excellent indeed," the young man concludes. He adds that this was the one subject which called for any display of talent by the members in that session, adding that "there was too much unanimity among them to have elicited all the strength of any one of them."

Young Dabney Carr, Jefferson's brother-in-law, newly elected member, moved the adoption of the resolutions, which passed unanimously. Mr. Carr impressed himself on the members as a man of talent and great charm. He died less than two months after the House had adjourned, and he was a real loss to his country, in the judgment of those who had come to know him, especially the members of the standing committee, who had had the opportunity to see him at work.

Incidentally, while Henry was holding forth with all his skill against the King and his Ministry in his speech for the passage of the resolutions, a number of spectators in the gallery, the moment he ended, leaped to their feet and hurtled out of the chamber. For a few moments it was feared that there was a fire, but no. The men had rushed up the stair leading to the top of the cupola and torn down the royal flag, which flew in the breeze there when the Assembly was in session, taken it to a well into which they doused it. Tucker certainly missed out in the choice of speakers he made.

Having finished everything it had on hand, the House now, with a probable inner grin, presented the Address written several days ago to the Governor on March 15th. Here it is:

My Lord: We, his Majesty's dutiful subjects, beg leave to present to your Excellency our sincere thanks for your attention to the interests of this colony by vigorously endeavoring to bring the forgers of our paper currency to justice, but the proceedings in this case, my Lord, though rendered necessary by the particular nature of it, are nevertheless different from the usual mode, it being regular that an examining court on criminals should be held, either in the county where the act was committed, or the arrest made. The duty we owe our constituents, my Lord, obliges us to be as attentive to the safety of the innocent as we are desirous of punishing the guilty; and we apprehend that a doubtful construction and various execution of criminal law does greatly endanger the safety of innocent men. We do therefore most humbly pray your Excellency that the proceedings in this case may not, in the future, be drawn into consequence or example.

Henry, conceded to be the greatest criminal lawyer in the Colony, was doubtless the author of this neat rebuke. Both the resolves and this Address said what they wanted to say, but so cleverly that they could not be drawn into any charge of being treasonable, or as Lee put it in a letter written a month later to the Pennsylvanian, John Dickinson, "Our language is so contrived as to prevent the enemies of America from bringing this transaction into the vortex of treason, whither they have carried every honest attempt to defend ourselves from their tyrannous designs to destroy our constitutional liberty."

Following the reception of the Address the Governor made the Assembly "a rude speech," and dissolved them. It was exactly what they'd expected. Next day the Committee of Correspondence met in a room at the Raleigh to prepare a circular addressed to the Speakers of the other colonial assemblies, inclosing with each a copy of the resolutions, and also a copy of the Act they had passed against forging and circulating counterfeit money, asking that a similar Act be passed for the protection of all. This was the first invitation to united legislation.

The responses that came back to the Speaker in Virginia were heartening. Many of them were full of praises to Virginia for this happy inauguration of a real intercommunication. And a newspaper, the *New Hampshire Gazette* flew high with this piece of comment: "Heaven itself seems to have dictated it (the plan) to the noble Virginians. O Americans, embrace this plan of union as your life! It will work out your political salvation."

England felt the impact of this new move; says William Lee, writing from London on January 1, 1774: "It struck a greater panic into the Ministers than anything that has taken place since the Stamp Act."

The year 1773 was not to depart without one more happening that history never forgets. On December 16th Boston held her greatest of all tea parties, and doubtless the only one where not a single drop of tea was drunk.

Chapter 11

HENRY ADDRESSES THE FIRST CONTINENTAL CONGRESS

DRIVEN by the King on one side, and on the other by the desperate situation of the India Company, with seven million pounds of tea in its warehouses and no place to go, Lord North thought up a new scheme to drag taxes from the colonies. A tax of threepence a pound would be charged in America, while at the same time all duties payable in England by the Company would be remitted. They would thus be able to sell tea, tax and all, under the prevailing price.

Four cities were picked to receive the first consignments, many hundreds of pounds; they were Boston, New York, Philadelphia, and Charleston. When the news reached the

colonies, wrath flamed. Also, the plan for mutual inter-
action showed its worth. The Correspondence Committees
agreed on united action in support of whatever colony or
colonies were singled out for oppression. Then, as the time
approached when the ships might be expected, each of the
four cities took action. In Philadelphia a great mass meeting demanded of the consignees the surrender of their
commissions, which would prevent their accepting the
cargo. Taking a look at the aroused Quakers milling about
in the City of Brotherly Love, the consignees gracefully
complied. Charleston pursued the same course with the
same result, and New York, at a crowded meeting in the
City Hall, announced that not a leaf of tea should be
permitted to pollute their fair city. But when Boston took
like measures she received a slap in the face from her
governor. So the wild Indians, or excellent imitations of
them, boarded the vessel and tossed all the tea into the
harbor, where the fishes might make the best they could
of it.

Henry was in Williamsburg at this time to attend the
sittings of the General Court, where he was handling all
Robert Carter Nicholas's cases as well as his own. Nicholas
was too much occupied with being Treasurer of the Colony to attend to this law business, and chose Henry to take
over for him, a signal compliment from a lawyer so re-
nowned as Nicholas. The news of the action by the cities
to whom the tea had been sent, and of Boston's picturesque
behavior, reached Henry at the capital, therefore, and he
was able to discuss with the Correspondence Committee
members what plans should be adopted later on.

Meanwhile the pestiferous Governor had been in a peck
of trouble over the boundary line between Virginia and
Pennsylvania, concerning which there had been some dis-

pute, Pennsylvania claiming her southern boundary was the 39th parallel, while Virginia insisted on the Monongahela River, having built Fort Pitt (Pittsburgh to-day) on that stream. The dispute had already been referred to the King, but Lord Dunmore took a company of soldiers with him during the past summer and tried to oust the Pennsylvanians from the land about the Fort. Result was the death of several friendly Ohio Indians, and the loss of their homes and tempers to the Whites. By spring the Indians were on the warpath, and my Lord was getting nervous. Now, when his Colony was seething with political excitement, and as the peril of an Indian invasion increased, he called the Assembly to meet on May 5, 1774. This summons suited the Virginians to perfection.

In his Address to the House Dunmore demanded that regular forces should be raised, the disputed territory taken over, and the Indians defeated. But the Assembly in words gentle and courteous, refused. The King, they told him, could be left to judge the boundary dispute, and there were enough men already under arms to take care of the Indians.

The House then turned its attention to various local affairs and business on hand, to get that out of the way before taking up the tea situation. They had barely started on this routine work, however, before news arrived that the Port of Boston was to be closed, the Army and Navy to enforce the decree and see to it that all commerce in and out of the city was prevented, the decree to take force on June 1st.

This was fighting talk and Henry and his immediate group decided that something to arouse and shock the people must be found. As Jefferson puts it, "the lead in the House in these subjects being no longer left to the old members, Mr. Henry, R. H. Lee, F. L. Lee, three or four others and myself," must meet and give the answer.

They met in the Council room of the Capitol, because of its fine library. Here they sought through various authors for a precedent of what was in their minds. They found it in a volume of Rushworth.

"Somewhat modernizing Rushworth's language," Jefferson goes on, "we cooked up a resolution . . . for appointing the first day of June, on which the Port Bill was to commence, for a day of fasting, humiliation and prayer, to implore Heaven to avert from us the evils of civil war, to inspire us with firmness in support of our rights, and to turn the hearts of the King and Parliament to moderation and justice."

To give their plan all the impressiveness possible, they visited Mr. Nicholas next to beg him, because he was a man of "grave and religious character," to make the motion. He agreed, made it at the session that same day, and the resolution passed without opposition. It was now the 24th of May.

Next it was agreed that on June 1st the Burgesses were to be in their seats at the Capitol by ten in the morning, and then to proceed, led by the Speaker carrying the mace, along Duke of Gloucester Street to the church, where the Reverend Mr. Price would read the prayers and preach the sermon.

The Williamsburg *Gazette* published all this May 26. Immediately the expected became fact. A messenger from the Governor arrived at the Hall where the Burgesses were in session, summoning them to attend the Governor in the Council Chamber. By twos and threes they entered, conversing amiably in low tones, quiet, orderly, inwardly amused. Lord Dunmore was being true to type.

The Governor glared at them:

"Mr. Speaker and Gentlemen of the House of Burgesses. I have in my hand"—he shook it at them—"a paper published by the order of your House, conceived in such terms as reflect highly upon his Majesty and the Parliament of Great Britain, which makes it necessary for me to dissolve you; and you are dissolved accordingly."

They had been in session just three weeks. Now they adjourned to the Raleigh where they drew up a carefully considered paper, copies of which would be sent to all the Corresponding Committees. In it they rehearsed Britain's actions against the freedom of the colonies, expressed the opinion that tea should not be used by any person wishing well to the rights of America, and, since it was the India Company which had sent the taxed tea, that nothing, except saltpeter and spices, coming from that Company ought to be purchased.

Then came the truly important portion of their paper. It was a recommendation that deputies from each colony meet annually in some selected place, to deliberate as might be required on the united interests of America. Ever since the somewhat abortive Stamp Act Congress there had been in the thoughts of several leaders in different colonies the idea that such gatherings would be of value; but this was the first proposal for an annual and therefore regular meeting as part of the necessary proceedings in achieving united action by all the colonies.

The paper concluded with this greeting, not without its concealed threat to Britain, nor yet its glint of humor:

A tender regard for the interests of our fellow subjects, the merchants and manufacturers of Great Britain, prevents us from going farther at this time; most earnestly hoping that the unconstitutional principle of taxing the colonies without their consent will not be persisted in, thereby to compel us against our will to avoid all commercial intercourse with Britain. Wishing them and our people free and happy, we are their affectionate friends, the late representatives of Virginia.

The paper was signed by the Speaker and every member of the House, together with several clergymen and other men of high standing. It was published in the *Gazette*.

George Mason, who was to be one of Henry's lasting friends, had arrived in Williamsburg a few days before this climax on some business concerning his charter rights. Mason still kept out of public life, preferring his home, study, managing the great and rich plantation he owned, and visits to the capital during sessions to meet his friends and listen to the proceedings of the House when something interesting was going on. It was not until next year that he finally permitted himself to be elected a member of the House. Jefferson speaks of him as "a man of the first order of wisdom among those who acted on the theater of the Revolution." Mason was nearing fifty at this time, his dark hair touched with gray, a tall, athletically-built man, with a grave, handsome face and brilliant black eyes. His whole bearing was lofty and commanding.

Writing to a friend, Martin Cockburn, on this eventful May 26th, he says that every one was so occupied with the situation in Boston that he would not be able to get his business attended to for several days. Then he tells of meeting Henry:

Whatever resolves and measures are intended for the preservation of our rights and liberties are conducted and prepared with a great deal of privacy and by very few members, of whom Patrick Henry is the principal. At the request of the gentlemen concerned I have spent an evening with them... and I had an opportunity of conversing with Mr. Henry and knowing his sentiments; as well as hearing him speak in the

House on different occasions. He is by far the most powerful speaker I ever heard. Every word he says not only engages, but commands the attention, and your passions are no longer your own when he addresses them. He is in my opinion the first man upon this continent, as well in abilities as in public virtue.

The Virginian proposal for a General Congress was agreed to with enthusiasm by all the colonies. September 4th was selected as the date, and Philadelphia as the place of meeting. A building known as Carpenters Hall was offered the delegates by its owners and builders, the Master-Carpenters of Philadelphia, fine, substantial men glad to lend their Hall for such a use, although warned by the strong royalist element in the city that "Your necks may be lengthened beyond convenience if you don't look out." Great builders, these Carpenters, direct descendants in trade inheritance and traditions from the Worshipful Company of Carpenters founded in London in 1477. The bricks used in the building came from England, the mortar that held them together could not be broken except by a granite cutter; in its proportions, the grace of its cupola, over which on a staff gleamed a copper ball, its fine entrance, its handsome windows that gave to the east on Dock Street, in all its structure the Hall was worthy of the use to which it was to be put. To-day it stands stout and noble as ever, and still called Carpenters Hall.

On May 28th a ball was given by Williamsburg in honor of Lady Dunmore, recently arrived from New York—a gala affair, in the Hall of the Capitol, attended by every one of importance in the town, either citizen or visitor. All was light, laughter, music, stately dancing, carriages coming and going, fine costumes. The Governor and the dissolved

Burgesses may have ignored each other but the tense undercurrents were kept submerged. Only the day before the noble Lord had within hearing of a number of people, when Patrick Henry passed on his way to the Capitol, growled, "That fellow's the most dangerous man in the Colony," hate contorting his face; but now Henry danced with the young ladies of Williamsburg society at the party given the Governor's Lady as though Lord Dunmore had not been defied nor himself and his companions dissolved.

On the fourth day following came the Day of Mourning. As had been said, so it was done. All flags—excepting the one over the Governor's Palace—were at half-mast. At ten the deep voice of Bruton Church's great bell began to toll, the echoes spreading from church to church in imperceptible waves over the fair Virginia country. "The effect," Jefferson tells us, "was like a shock of electricity."

The service over, most of the delegates returned to their homes, having agreed to meet on August 1st, of this year 1774, to choose the deputies to the General Convention. When that time came they sat for six days, reaching certain agreements, the more important being that after November 1st nothing more, excepting medicines, should be bought from Britain, that no more slaves would be permitted to land in the Colony, and that after August 10, 1775, neither tobacco or any other article should be exported to England. This date was set because a deal of labor had already been expended on next year's crop, work that had "prevented the colonists from pursuing other methods of clothing and supporting their families."

Next came the selection of the deputies and the writing of a spirited set of *Instructions* for them. The seven men chosen were Peyton Randolph, Patrick Henry, George

Washington, Richard Bland, Richard Henry Lee, Edmund Pendleton, and Benjamin Harrison. Each had his special qualifications, and between them they expressed the entire Colony. The *Instructions* summarized Virginia's attitude, including one old cause of irritation which had not till then found expression. "Wanting the protection of Britain," it ran, "we have long acquiesced in the Acts of Navigation, restrictive of our commerce, which we considered as an ample recompense for such protection; but as those Acts derive their efficacy from that foundation alone, we have reason to expect they will be restrained, so as to produce the reasonable purpose of Britain and not be injurious to us."

On their way next month to the Congress, Pendleton and Henry rode together, and were both invited by Washington to stop overnight at Mount Vernon, when he would join them for the rest of the journey. They arrived in the afternoon and were welcomed on the veranda, where cool drinks and slight refreshments were waiting.

"Sit down and refresh yourselves, gentlemen," Washington begged. "Martha and I are in the habit of taking tea out here at this time, but that's over for the present. For how long, who shall say?" and he gave Henry an interrogative glance as they took their seats.

Henry shook his head, his brows contracted:

"I can't see England yielding her demands upon us in any near future. Now that General Gage has been sent, together with four regiments, as Governor of Massachusetts and Commander-in-Chief for North America, with tyrannical powers, we must expect to see these powers exerted in the effort to bring us to our knees. It'll only be when we prove we won't bend them," and he gave his swift, slight smile, "that England, for the sake of her own commerce if for no higher motive, may cease her oppression."

The two other men agreed that this was sound sense.

"We are facing serious issues," Pendleton said. "But we must remember we have friends in England, powerful friends. Pitt, Burke, Dowdeswell, and others. They will be working for us, as will the stern measures we are ourselves determined to carry through. The great necessity is that the colonies support each other heart and soul."

"I've heard from more than one in the House, Henry," Washington told him, "that our practically unbroken unity is largely due to you. We shall count upon you to establish the same harmony at the Convention. And now, if you feel like it, let me show you a stallion I bought last summer. He's a magnificent creature."

Washington was as fond of hunting and fishing as Patrick, and a great lover of horses, racing his own at the Williamsburg track with considerable success.

Next morning, early, the men took their leave of Martha Washington, who had come out on the veranda to bid them godspeed.

"I hope you stand firm," were her final words. "I know George will."

At the appointed hour on September 4, 1774, in Carpenters Hall, the Continental Congress met for the first time. The great Hall we see to-day was then divided by a partition, the delegates occupying the main room, with its twelve twelve-paned windows and its one fan window, honoring the thirteen colonies. The House was organized for business with all the solemn dignity of a regular Legislature. Peyton Randolph of Virginia was chosen President.

It was in truth a tremendous moment in history. Here for the first time the great men of the different colonies came together, many among them never having met before, to join in the labor of saving and establishing the liberties of three million people, with all their posterity. Their councils would determine the fate of America for many generations. Should these men not prove wise nor strong enough there were no others to turn to, and the cause was lost.

The preliminaries over, a deep and what seemd a long silence fell upon these men, sitting together in the great room, on the point of starting—who could predict what?

Each man looked at his neighbor with hesitation, with doubt, with anxiety; but not one seemed willing to start the great ball—a nation's ball—rolling. The silence became a weight, an oppression.

And then Patrick Henry rose slowly to his feet and looked about him.

A tall, slender figure, with shoulders slightly stooped, wearing a dark gray costume resembling a Presbyterian clergyman's attire, and a dark wig, he stepped slowly forward so that he might turn and face the audience. He began, slowly, hesitatingly, as was so often the case with him, expressing his regret that he did not have the power to be equal to this moment, could not do it justice. Many in the audience did not know who he was, yet, listening even to the first halting sentences, felt that he translated their own sense of hesitancy, their own inadequacy, and their emotion was touched.

Then his genius stirred, lighting his face, lifting his frame so that he seemed suddenly to dominate all those gazing eyes. His power grew as he warmed to his subject, his voice, his gestures, his words uniting into a single overpowering expression, mastering every eye, every ear, every heart. He spoke easily, fluently, clearly, not raising his voice, whose carrying pitch was marvelous, not straining his points, yet handling his theme with a variety, a color, a passion that kept his audience as amazed as they were intent. There was grandeur in him, and those who listened knew an answering grandeur.

Henry's theme he put in these words:

"I go upon the assumption that government is at an end. All distinctions are thrown down; all America is thrown into one mass. We must aim at the minutiae of rectitude. America must now provide her own government. The distinctions between Virginians, Pennsylvanians, New Yorkers and New Englanders are no more. I am not a Virginian, but an American."

The question before the Congress to which Henry spoke was how the colonies should vote. Should votes be counted by colonies, by poll or by interests? A difficult question. If by colonies, then the little ones carried the same weight as the large ones. If by poll, then the smaller delegations from smaller colonies would make the result unjust. If by the importance and variety of their interests, the deputies knew of no data by which these could be measured for each colony.

"If the freemen can be represented by their numbers," Henry said, "we should be satisfied. It is, however, well-nigh impossible to determine either the strength in population or in wealth of each colony. The representatives of each, however, have been chosen by the freemen of that colony, and if each colony casts one vote, through its deputies, we shall get a fair expression of the whole."

The resolution finally adopted carried this out, as the only possible solution.

But Henry's speech, as a whole, swept far above this. He spoke, and for the first time in this world, as an American to Americans. He made his hearers feel the creative greatness of this fact. Americans, met together to keep America free. Americans, who would not suffer any king or any government to assault that freedom, that liberty for which their forefathers had fought and died through the centuries, and which it was their own God-given duty to treasure and preserve, anywhere in their country, won from the wilderness with hardship and suffering, where danger threatened. Could men come together in a loftier cause?

He stirred their souls, but he was wise, and knew that there were many men in that Congress, men of high influence, who did not feel as he did. He did not scold or bully nor make use of his marvelous powers of invective. No. Henry wanted to keep these men together, not force them apart. He was right, for later some of these very men joined the glorious vanguard of patriots, bringing their followers with them. He knew the Congress was taking the first steps toward war. But he did not say it then.

He finished and sat down, to rolling waves of applause. All over men questioned "Who is he?" or murmured one to another, "It's Patrick Henry, of course. I've heard of him, but never heard him till now. There's no other orator in this world can touch him." Even the men there who had heard him speak in Virginia were amazed afresh. One man, Robert Atkinson, writing home to Petersburg, called him a "Son of Thunder."

The Congress did not adjourn until October 26, agreeing on May 10, 1775, for the next get-together. Committees were appointed to meet and discuss various points on

which a general agreement must be reached, and either
Patrick Henry or R. C. Lee served on most of those, and
often both served, where the work to be done was particularly important. On those committees where neither
of these two was represented, there was some other Virginian delegate, a witness to the important position the
Colony held in the minds of the others. The report on the
Rights of the Colonies, where Henry's resolutions in regard to the Stamp Act were practically adopted as he wrote
them; another reporting on the statutes affecting trade
and manufactures in the colonies; a third which contained
the important petition to the King; these serve to show
the breadth of his activities. The papers thus drawn up
during the weeks through which the different committee
members met, are of a very high order. Pitt, Lord Chatham, who was back in his place in the House of Lords had
this to say:

When your lordships look at the papers transmitted to us
from America, when you consider their decency, firmness and
wisdom, you cannot but respect their cause, and wish to make
it your own... For myself, I must declare and avow... that
for solidity of reasoning, force of sagacity, and wisdom of conclusion under such a complication of difficult circumstances,
no nation, or body of men can stand in preference to the
General Congress at Philadelphia. I trust it is obvious to your
lordships that all attempts to impose servitude on such men, to
establish a despotism over such a mighty nation, must be vain,
must be fatal.

While the Congress was going forward with its work,
Governor Dunmore had managed to start his Indian war.
Two members of the Assembly, General Andrew, and
Colonel Charles, Lewis, were ordered to march at the head
of one body of troops via the Kanawha to its juncture with
the Ohio, and there to await the Governor, at the head of

another and larger body, who was to proceed via Fort Pitt, renamed by him Fort Dunmore. General Lewis reached the rendezvous on October 1st, but there was no sign of Dunmore, who should have been the first to arrive.

There was nothing for it but to wait, a dangerous business in Indian country. Not until the 9th was word received from his Lordship, when a messenger arrived bringing orders that Lewis was to take his command across a trackless wilderness to a Shawnee village on Scioto Creek, where Dunmore would meet him.

"The man's up to some mischief," General Lewis confided to his brother. "The Indians are fairly sure to know where we are, and if we move into that wilderness they can ambush and surround us. I don't like it."

"Neither do I. But what are we to do?"

That question was solved the next day, when a compact little army of various tribes headed by the Shawnees, attacked at dawn. After a bitter battle, and though outnumbered, the two Lewises and their men routed, and almost entirely destroyed the attackers. So thorough was the defeat that this was the last time Indians attacked in that part of the country east of the Ohio.

The victorious Virginians returned to Williamsburg by mid-December to find the Governor already there. His surprise at seeing them could not be hidden, and his excuses for failing to make the rendezvous sounded hollow. It looked very much as though his lordship had expected the Indians to account for them, ridding his Colony of men whom he well knew to be against him.

A short while earlier the Virginian members of the General Congress had returned home, all except one among them highly confident of the success sure to follow the receipt of their deliberations and the various messages and addresses sent to England. Richard Henry Lee expressed this conviction in these buoyant words:

"We shall infallibly carry all our points...all the offensive acts will be repealed; the army and the fleet will be recalled, and Britain will give up her foolish project."

He was speaking to John Adams, of Massachusetts, who answered gravely, "I hope so."

He may have hoped so, but he did not think so, as he revealed in a private talk with Patrick Henry, before the two men separated, each to carry on the work for freedom in their separate colonies. Writing to a friend, Adams quotes the substance of this talk as follows:

I expressed a full conviction that our resolves, our declaration of rights, etc., however they might be expected by the people of America, and however necessary to cement the union of the colonies, would be but waste paper in England. Mr. Henry...agreed with me that they would be totally lost on the government, however they might impress the people of England. I had just received a short and hasty letter from Major Joseph Hawley of Northampton, Virginia, containing a few broken hints, as he called them, of what he thought was proper to be done, and concluding with these words "After all, we must fight." This letter I read to Henry, and as soon I pronounced the words (as above) he raised his head, and with an energy and vehemence I shall never forget, broke out, *'By God, I am of that man's mind.'*

Two against the many. Adams in the north, Patrick in the south, each great, each powerful, each devoted. It proved enough.

Adams was the more deeply impressed by Henry's response to Major Hawley's letter because it was common knowledge that in an age when swearing was usual Patrick never took the Lord's name in vain.

His response was nothing less than a solemn dedication and avowal. Among all the men to whom I spoke he stood alone in his conviction that we would have to fight. Lee represented the mind of the convention as a whole. Washington never spoke in public, but in private he expressed the opinion that with the adoption of the non-importation as well as the non-exportation decisions, we should prevail. To my thinking, Henry was the only man who appeared to me sensible of the precipice, or rather, the pinnacle on which we stood, and had candor and courage enough to avow it.

A strong and enduring friendship had sprung up between Patrick and the two Adams', John and his second cousin, Samuel, during their weeks together at the Congress.

Chapter 12

THE GREAT SPEECH IN ST. JOHN'S CHURCH

REACHING home, Henry found the people generally indignant over the Governor's continued proroguing of the Assembly. His lordship was still away, supposedly fighting the Indians, and everything was in confusion, with the courts all over the Colony suspended because the Act for negotiating and collecting officers' fees had lapsed. Dunmore got back to Williamsburg early in December, but still refused to call the Assembly to meet. It was, of course, never to meet again.

In Hanover Henry suggested that the people come together in committees in each county, leading the way in his own county, which appointed its committee early in November. These committees, Hanover's example having been followed all over the Colony, took over the necessary functions of government, adopting the title *Committees of Safety,* and carried on through the ever increasing confusion of the coming months.

That started, Patrick's next move was to call the militia of Hanover County to meet at the Smith Tavern, later known by the gay name of "Merry Oaks," near Hanover Court House, where he would address them on a matter of the first importance. A large number arrived on the given date and heard what is described by Charles Dabney, one of them, as a most animated speech.

"It appears likely we shall have to take to arms to defend our rights," Henry told the gathering, "and our first care must be to form ourselves into a volunteer company." It was no use waiting until they lost their freedom before arming to prevent that loss. Training was necessary, and the very fact that they were training would be a warning that the Congress had meant what it said.

The list was opened for signatures, and a great part of the young men who had come to hear his call, enrolled themselves as volunteers. It was decided that when enough had joined to form a company, they should choose their own officers. There was plenty of enthusiasm, gay talk, some solemnity, jolly toasts at the tavern. This was the first of Virginia's volunteer companies, and was presently to attract the notice of the rest of the American colonies. By the end of December six or seven other counties in Virginia had followed suit, upon which, with a good deal of exaggeration, Dunmore wrote to England that "every county is now arming a company of men whom they call an independent company." The movement didn't go as fast as that. The Committees of Safety were working well, they had no need of military coöperation, and the general

feeling remained that England would yield to the demands
made by the Congress. In February they began to doubt
this happy outcome when a savage speech by King George
in opening Parliament at the year's beginning reached
America. England then, moreover, had not yet received
news of the doings of the Congress, was reacting only to
the non-importation agreements. When it did hear what
had been decided upon, in spite of strong demands from
merchants and manufacturers for conciliatory action, the
King insisted that nothing should be yielded, at the same
time making a very gracious response to the Petition to
him which Mr. Dickinson had written for the Committee
in the General Congress. A letter from England by one of
the gossips of the court, dated December 14th, carried this
news of the King's pleasure, with information that it
seemed certain all "but one or two" of the Acts would be
repealed. The facts, however, were different. Parliament,
still in session when the Second Virginia Convention met,
March 20, 1775, was busy refusing to adopt Lord Chatham's motion to remove the soldiers from Boston, in spite
of the splendid speech with which he supported it, and
voting that all commerce should end and that the whole
American population, omitting only the proved royalists,
should be declared traitors and rebels. Later an amend-
ment was adopted that those rebels who repented, *excepting some twenty*, in which Patrick Henry's name led all
the rest, might be pardoned.

Unaware of all this, happy at the King's nice words,
quoted in the letter just published in the *Gazette*, and
generally feeling assured that the demands made by the
General Congress would be granted, the members met this
second time in a mood of hope which they expressed in
sweet talk. It was generally affirmed and agreed to that "It

is the ardent wish of this Colony, and we are persuaded of the whole continent of North America, to see a speedy return of those halcyon days when we lived a free and happy people," etc., etc. This sort of wish-wash had been in progress for three days when Henry, thoroughly bored by it, rose, to say something of a different nature. He moved three plain-talk resolutions:

1: *Resolved,* That a well-regulated militia, composed of gentlemen and yeomen, is the natural strength and only security of a free government; that such a militia in this country would forever render it unnecessary for the mother country to keep among us, for the purposes of our defense, any standing army of mercenary soldiers, always subversive of the quiet, and dangerous to the liberties, of the people, and would obviate the pretext of taxing us for their support.

2: *Resolved,* That the establishment of such militia is, at this time, peculiarly necessary, by the state of our laws for the protection and defense of the country, some of which have already expired, and others will shortly do so; and that the known remissness of the government in calling us together in legislative capacity renders it too insecure in this time of danger and distress, to rely that opportunity will be given of renewing them, in general assembly, or making any provision to secure our inestimable rights and liberties from those further violations with which they are threatened.

3: *Resolved,* therefore, that this colony be immediately put into a state of defense, and that (blank) be a committee to prepare a plan for embodying, arming and disciplining such a number of men as may be sufficient for that purpose.

The sweet calm of the three preceding days vanished with an agonized gulp.

The first resolution was well enough; it was taken from one passed by the Maryland convention last December, and Fairfax County had adopted a like paper drawn by George Mason and presented by George Washington. But the two last, and especially that dreadful number three! Up started Colonel Richard Bland, Mr. Nicholas, Treasurer of the Colony, Edmund Pendleton, and several other rich planters who were desperately against any such plan. Why, no public man had dared suggest such a thing as war with Britain except—except—well, only as distantly possible. And just now, when his Majesty had been so gracious! Henry was a madman. With what would the colonies wage war? Tell us that. Where are our stores, our arms, our generals, our money, our sinews of war? One by one they had their say. Think, think, they implored, of the strength we derive from being connected with Great Britain. Think of all the pleasant things that are ours because of this connection, and which will vanish if we plunge into war. Yet Henry had tossed aside all the cautious *perhapses* and *let's hopes*.

There were men there who were jealous of Henry. He gleamed too bright in the eyes of the people. They would welcome having him thrust down, relegated to the background. Others were frankly fearful. After all, Great Britain *was* great. Her navies, her armies, all ready, all armed, and America with no more than a cudgel or two to defy her, to brave her!

It is human to think that things will get better, that relief is in sight, that to plunge toward danger is mere foolhardiness. We have seen that in this day, God knows. Voice after voice in that gathering of men in the quiet old church was heard, counseling patience, saying the King had had a change of heart, hinting at the impossibilities confronting a country like theirs against such a colossus as Great Britain. No man remembered David, with his sling, walking out to meet Goliath.

Obviously the only thing for Henry to do was to withdraw his resolutions and steal away with them, unwept, unhonored, and unsung. But this was precisely what he had no intention in the world of doing. He had not written them on the spur of the moment, hastily, thoughtlessly. He had given them long thought, and they grew from the very deeps of his conviction. He knew the colonies must fight, or lose their freedom. The men now misguiding England would not draw back. He could read their minds and their hearts as easily as though they were in this church with him, as, all his life, he was able to read men.

At last the opponents to his measures ended and Henry rose to reply. He rose with a lofty dignity, and the Convention fell utterly silent. He looked quietly about him at all the faces turned upon him, and then he lifted his head and looked off, above all the heads, and there was about him a majesty. He stood at ease, and one might have thought that it was Fate who met his gaze, and that the two knew each other.

He began to speak, dropping his gaze to the audience, and his voice was gentle:

"No man, Mr. President, thinks more highly than I of the patriotism, as well as of the abilities of the honorable gentlemen who have just addressed the House. But different men often see the same subject in different lights. Therefore I hope it will not be thought disrespectful of me if, entertaining, as I do, opinions of a character opposite to theirs, I should speak forth my sentiments freely and without reserve. This is no time for ceremony. The question before the House is one of awful moment to this country. For my own part, I consider it as a question of nothing less than freedom or slavery; and in proportion to the magnitude of the subject ought to be the freedom of the debate. It is only in this way that we can hope to arrive at truth, and fulfil the great responsibility which we owe to God and our Country. Should I keep back my opinion at such a time through fear of giving offense I would consider myself as guilty of treason towards my country, and of an act of disloyalty to the majesty of Heaven, which I revere above all earthly kings."

Again Henry's eyes swept the faces of the men, all of whom were listening intently, and then, with a slight shrug of the shoulders, he continued:

"Mr. President, it is natural to man to indulge in the illusions of hope. We are apt to shut our eyes against a painful truth, and listen to the song of that siren, till she transforms us into beasts. Is this the part of wise men engaged in a great and arduous struggle for liberty?" The speaker's voice began to take on a sterner note. "Are we disposed to be of the number of those who, having eyes see not, and having ears hear not those things which so nearly concern their temporal salvation? For my part, whatever anguish of spirit it may cost, I am willing to know the whole truth. To know the worst, and to provide for it.

"I have but one lamp by which my feet are guided, and that is the lamp of experience. I know of no way of judging a future but by the past. And judging by the past, I wish to know what there has been in the conduct of the British Ministry for the last ten years, to justify those hopes with which gentlemen have been pleased to solace themselves in the House. Is it that insidious smile with which our Petition has been received? Trust it not, Sir. It will prove a snare. Suffer not yourselves to be betrayed by a kiss. Ask yourselves how this gracious reception of our Petition comports with those warlike preparations which cover our waters and darken our land. Are fleets and armies necessary to a work of love and reconciliation? Have we shown ourselves so unwilling to be reconciled that force must be called in to win back our love? Let us not deceive ourselves, Sir. These are the implements of war and subjugation—the last arguments to which kings resort. Can any gentleman assign any other possible motive? Has Great Britain an enemy in this quarter of the world to call for all this accumulation of navies and armies? No, Sir. She has none! They are meant for us— they can be meant for no other."

Patrick paused after each telling question for a pregnant moment, but only the deep silence of the audience in that church responded, a silence to be felt, a silence that clamored for him to continue. The hearers wanted his answer alone.

"Sir, they are sent over to bind and rivet upon us those chains which the British Ministry have been so long forging. And what have we to oppose them? Shall we try argument? Sir, we have been trying that for the last ten years. Have we anything new to offer upon the subject? Nothing. We have held the subject up in every light of which we are capable, but it has all been in vain. Shall we resort to entreaty and humble supplication? What terms shall we find that have not been already exhausted? Let us not, I beseech you, Sir, deceive ourselves any longer. Sir, we have done everything that could be done to avert the storm which is now coming on. We have petitioned, we have remonstrated, we have supplicated, we have prostrated ourselves before the throne and have implored its interposition to arrest the tyrannical hands of the Ministry and Parliament—" A hint of scorn sharpened Henry's voice. "Our petitions have been slighted; our remonstrances have produced additional violence and insult; our supplications have been disregarded, and we have been spurned, with contempt, from the foot of the throne. After all this, can we indulge the fond hope of peace and reconciliation? There is no longer any room for hope."

From this point on there was a mounting passion in Henry's voice; his face, his eyes, his gestures made one whole, a living whole, and in those brilliant eyes the flame seemed caught from very heaven.

"If we wish to be free, if we wish to preserve inviolate those privileges for which we have been so long contending, if we mean not basely to abandon the noble struggle in which we have been so long engaged and which we have pledged ourselves never to abandon until the glorious object of our contest shall be won—we must fight. I repeat it, Sir. We—Must—Fight. An appeal to arms and to the God of Hosts is all that is left us!

"They tell us, Sir, that we are weak; unable to cope with so terrible an enemy. But when shall we be stronger? Will it be the next week, or the next year? Will it be when we are totally disarmed and when a British guard shall be stationed in every house? Shall we gather strength from irresolution and inaction? Shall we acquire the means of resistance by lying supine and hugging the delusive phantom of hope until our enemies have bound us hand and foot?

"Sir, we are not weak, if we use those means which the God of nature hath placed in our power. Three millions of people armed in the holy cause of liberty, and in such a country as this which we possess, are invincible to any forces which our enemy can send against us. And, Sir, we shall not fight our battle alone. There is a just God who rules the destinies of nations and who will raise up friends to fight with us. The battle, Sir, is not to the strong alone; it is to the vigilant, the active, the brave. Moreover, Sir, we have no election. Were we base enough to desire it, it is now too late to retire from the contest. There is no retreat but to submission and slavery. Our chains are forged—their clanking may be heard on the plains of Boston. The war is inevitable. And let it come! I repeat it, Sir. Let it come!

"Gentlemen may cry, peace, peace—but there is no peace. The war is actually begun. The next gale sweeping from the north will bring to our ears the clash of resounding arms! Our brethren are already in the field. Why stand we idle here? What is it the gentlemen wish? What would they have? Is life so dear or peace so sweet as to be purchased at the price of chains and slavery? Forbid it, Almighty God. I know not what course others may take, but as for me, give me liberty—or give me death."

A great silence followed as Patrick Henry ended. With the last words he had thrown his lifted arms wide, his head raised, his gaze blazing upward. There he stood for an appreciable moment, noble, unafraid, scorning a life not free and great—a victor.

And if ever a silence were eloquent, then, at that instant in our history, the silence answering him was eloquent.

Richard Henry Lee then rose and made a short, good speech backing up Henry's resolutions, and was followed by General Thomas Nelson, who joined Henry so ardently that the timid ones were in agony again. Among other forthright remarks he declared, "I call God to witness that if any British troops should be landed within the country of which I am lieutenant, I will wait for no orders and will obey none which should forbid me to summon my militia and repel the invaders at the water's edge." Since Nelson was among the very wealthiest men in Virginia, who was to prove his patriotism not only in the field but by giving to the cause at one time $100,000, and at another a thousand horses, his example had a powerful effect on the rich men of the Colony.

Henry's resolutions passed unanimously, indeed, enthusiastically. A committee was named to carry out the plans they recommended, and it is interesting to note that among the members were several who had opposed Henry before he made his speech. The men selected for the committee were Patrick Henry, Richard C. Lee, Robert C. Nicholas, Ben Harrison, Lemuel Riddick, George Washington, Adam Stevens, Andrew Lewis, William Christian, Edmund Pendleton, Thomas Jefferson, Isaac Zane. They were all patriots, able, representative of the different groups in the Colony, and all had already opposed the demands of King and Parliament. The fact that several were more inclined to go slowly was no harm, for perhaps one or two wished to move too fast. In the end, accommodating themselves to each other, the one group by hastening, the other by retarding, they formed an excellent stand against Britain. They went to work immediately, reviving an old law of 1738 regarding the militia, which left them free to recommend the formation of infantry and cavalry troops in each county, to be properly armed and equipped, the arms, oddly to our ears, to include a tomahawk, arranging also for the collection of money to be spent on ammunition, and for the purchase of such ammunition. This business done, the Convention adjourned.

Among the many witnesses to the splendor of Henry's speech was a certain Colonel, Edward Carrington, who, reaching St. John's too late to make his way into the church, climbed up to seat himself on the sill of one of the open windows, where he was almost directly opposite the speaker. When Henry ended Carrington leaped down, and stamping on the turf beneath the window, exclaimed to some of his friends, his face full of joy and excitement, "When I die, I wish to be buried here, on this spot." And when he died, in 1810, there he was buried.

And meanwhile, in Parliament, in this same March, men were occupied in making plans far worse than perhaps even Henry anticipated. It is doubtful that he looked forward to having the whole country condemned as rebels even before war had been declared. Strange coincidence. The day before Henry spoke Edmund Burke made his famous speech to Commons introducing his resolutions for repealing all the hated laws against which the colonies were protesting. That speech, it has been said, would have placed him, had he never made another, in rank with the great orators of the world. But "Nobody minds you, Signor Benedick." Yet Henry was to give it the only possible answer the day following, three thousand miles away and weeks apart—the answer one brave and freedom-loving man expected from a brave and freedom-loving people, the answer he warned Britain she was certain to receive.

The fact that the speech Henry made that March day in 1775 has reached us almost intact and as he spoke it is due to two causes. One, the tremendous effect it produced on those who heard it, in that time of great stress and danger, so that sentence by sentence it remained sharp-cut in memory even after years had gone by. The talk was simple, straightforward, with a living passion breathing through it. In addition, there was Patrick Henry himself. Judge John Roane said that his "voice, countenance and gestures gave an irresistible force to his words which no description could convey." And many a man who heard him that day suddenly realized that the long-winded rhetoric and carefully polished periods of the other orators were bosh compared with such talk as this. All the pretty little rules so constantly studied, so constantly employed, what did they amount to? Edmund Randolph expressed that feeling when he asked whether all these rules "would not have choked his native fire?" He goes on in a kind of amazement, "It was Patrick Henry, born in obscurity, poor and without the advantage of literature, rousing the genius of his country and binding a band of patriots together to hurl defiance at so formidable a nation as Great Britain. This enchantment was spontaneous obedience to the working of the soul . . . Henry trampled on rules and yet triumphed."

Henry had "the advantage of literature" in spite of Mr. Randolph's remark, but when he spoke it did not enter his head to roll out quotations from the classics in the approved style. He stuck to his subject, using such words as most clearly defined it, and would bring others to see it and feel it as he did. One man said his language was "not unlike the New Testament." People in general who heard him at this and other times insisted that he was like St. Paul, in Athens, and "spoke as no man ever spoke before."

Here, then, were some of the reasons that this talk in especial was clearly remembered. The other cause we have to thank for having a great part of it, at least, is the careful work of William Wirt, Henry's first biographer, who took every trouble to interview those men who had heard Patrick on that day, and were still living. Their recollections resembled each other so nearly, that it cannot be doubted but that they were close to being exact.

And now forward to Revolution.

Chapter 13

TALE OF A GUNPOWDER PLOT

AT Concord, Massachusetts, on April 19, 1775, five hundred volunteers stopped and turned back the British force sent by General Gage to destroy the military stores in the village, and "By the rude bridge that arched the flood," the first British soldier was killed in the Revolutionary cause the embattled farmers were championing. On the day following, in Virginia, quite unaware of what had happened, Governor Dunmore sent orders to Captain Henry Collins, commanding the schooner *Magdalen*, lying at Burwell's Ferry, on the James, to enter Williamsburg that night and carry back with him twenty kegs of powder stored in the Powder Horn. This powder belonged to the people of Virginia and Dunmore had no mortal right to touch it.

Next morning every one in Williamsburg seemed to know of the robbery, and rage flamed. A number of the young and fiery got their guns, and possibly their tomahawks, shouting they were off to force Captain Collins to give that powder back or they'd blow up his ship. But cooler men begged them to wait until the Town Council could make itself heard, even then sitting to decide upon what measures to take. So the young men waited, strolling up and down, hanging close to where the pretty little building, surrounded by a brick wall, and looking like a sharply-pointed cap set on an eight-sided head with a single eye, stood in the midst of a small field.

Presently a deputation was sent by the Council to wait upon the Governor, carrying a communication addressed to him. It was respectfully worded, but firm. The powder had been stored in the Public Magazine, official title of the Powder Horn, because there had been very good reason to believe that certain vicious persons had been stirring up the Negroes, which might bring about an insurrection, and in that case it could be badly needed. Why had it been removed? And would the Governor have it, please, immediately returned?

The Governor retorted, his face growing purple, that he had received news of a rising in a neighboring county, and had moved it to a place of perfect security.

"If any need for it should arise, I am perfectly able to get it returned in an hour without any other assistance than my own servants; as to why it was removed by night, it was to prevent any such silly alarm as you are showing. I'm told that some of the people are under arms, which surprises me, but also makes it appear advisable not to put gunpowder in their hands."

With which sly dig he dismissed his callers.

**Governor Dunmore ordered Captain Collins to carry
back twenty kegs of powder.**

Several of Williamsburg's leading men, Peyton Randolph, Nicholas, and a few more, interviewed the leaders among the townsfolk and begged them to get the people quieted, as they were sure the powder would be returned. The day remained disturbed, but passed off, as did the following night, without any attempt at violence. Then, early the next morning the Governor sent a message to Randolph, Nicholas, and the others warning them that if any insult or injury were offered to himself, to his secretary, Captain Foy, or to Captain Collins, he would instantly declare the freedom of the slaves and burn all Williamsburg to ashes.

This absurd bluster infuriated every one, the news rapidly spreading over the whole Colony. Everywhere people became excited, there were meetings and threats. Williamsburg was especially disgusted because both Foy and Collins had been going about in the little city without any disagreeable incident, or the least affront to them having occurred.

But if a great many of the leading men in Virginia were not only angry at the theft of the gunpowder but, when it came to the elder brethren, a good deal alarmed by it, Patrick Henry felt very differently.

Speaking to two or three neighbors who had come to Scotchtown to find what he thought about the way the Governor was behaving, he answered most cheerfully:

"What do I think? I think it's the luckiest thing that could have happened to us."

"Lucky? How's that, Pat?"

"It's lucky because it will rouse the people in general as no tax on tea will ever do. When they hear of this robbery, and that the next step will most certainly be to disarm them completely, I tell you they'll jump to arms. They'll understand at once that if you disarm a man, you have him, being yourself armed, at your mercy. And they won't like it."

They didn't like it. At Fredericksburg, less than forty miles due north of Hanover, on the Rappahannock, men with arms in their hands were meeting, a large number of them. Henry decided to waste no time. He called the County Committee and the Hanover Volunteers to meet at the near-by small village of New Castle, and from this meetingplace, after discussion, sent a messenger to Williamsburg offering armed assistance. The messenger returned with a letter from Peyton Randolph next day, April 27th, reporting that all was quiet, that the Governor had pledged his honor to restore the powder, although he had not set any time for this action; but let's all keep calm, was the tenure of this communication. The same report was sent to Washington, at Fredericksburg, who then advised the men there against marching on Williamsburg.

But alas and woe! On April 29th the *Gazette* published the news of the British march on Concord and its final retreat through Lexington back to Boston. Two lives had been lost and many had been wounded on the American side.

As soon as the *Gazette's* news reached Henry, who was about to leave for the meeting of Congress on May 10th in Philadelphia, he decided it was time to stop waiting for the men in Williamsburg to start anything against the Governor, and why shouldn't his County of Hanover make the first move? Leaving later he would miss only the preliminaries.

He went out to ask the Volunteers, still camping near-by, what they thought? Was the gunpowder theirs, and should they rescue it? He asked it with his wonted vim and picturesqueness:

"The British Ministry means to rob us of all means to defend ourselves. Here in our colony you know what Governor Dunmore has done. Far to the north in Massachusetts, you've just heard what's happened there. The attempt to steal the powder in Concord was stopped—and Americans died to stop it. What do you want us to do? Do you want to live free, and hand freedom down to your children? Or do you prefer to become hewers of wood and drawers of water to these British Lordlings, tools of a corrupt, tyrannical Ministry? Make your choice—the one or the other, there is no middle way. If you basely forswear your freedom and choose the role of bondsmen, I need not tell you what life will be for us. Nay, turn the other way! Come and stand with me on Pisgah and gaze out upon the promised land, a land of plenty which with God's help, we can win. But we cannot wait, we cannot linger. Let us by fast and vigorous motion march on to Williamsburg and there compel either the restoration of the powder, or else seize the King's revenues in the hands of his Receiver-General, and so fairly balance the account. In doing this, men, you, the Hanover Volunteers, will have the chance of striking the first blow in this Colony for the great cause of American liberty, and will bring glory upon yourselves."

There was a roar of applause. The wildly cheering men then elected Henry to be their captain by acclamation. He accepted the honor with a few simple words, and immediately appointed Ensign Parke Goodall, one of his intimate friends, to take sixteen men with him and go to Laneville, in King Williams County, and there to march to the residence of Colonel Richard Corbin, who was acting as the

King's Receiver-General, and demand from him three hundred and thirty pounds sterling as compensation for the powder. Should he refuse, he was to be taken prisoner by Goodall and brought to Doncastle's Inn, in New Kent, sixteen miles from Williamsburg, where Henry and the rest of the volunteers would be waiting.

Mr. Goodall was presently on his way and the following morning Henry marched at the head of a hundred and fifty men, each fully armed.

The news of all this raced ahead like wildfire, and all along the way new recruits kept joining the marching force. By the time they reached New Kent there were close to five thousand in line.

The same day on which Henry spoke to the volunteers at New Castle, Lord Dunmore called the Council to meet with him at the Palace, fearing to go to the Capitol. There he stormed at them, telling them that he was right, every one else wrong, that the ridiculous excitement was due to a few "headstrong and designing persons, by whom plans and schemes are doubtless meditated in this Colony for subverting the present and erecting a new form of government." Then he went on to personal abuse of Patrick Henry. It was Henry who was the rebel and the author of all the trouble—what's more, a coward, afraid to go to the so-called Continental Congress with Randolph and Pendleton, "because he knows that if I get my hands on him, the scoundrel will get what he richly deserves, a rebel's punishment."

He ended with the demand that a Proclamation be made on the following day making clear exactly how his lordship felt and what he intended to do.

And every member of the Council humbly acquiesced, excepting only Mr. John Page, the one young man in the bunch of them. He refused, and was never afterward asked to join the meetings of the Council, which at that time consisted of Thomas Nelson, Sr., Richard Corbin, William Byrd, Ralph Wormley, Jr., and the Reverend John Camm, already known for his desperate attempts to get tobacco instead of money from the colonists, when tobacco had turned to gold. Mr. Nelson was the uncle of General Nelson, and none too pleased with the way the Governor was behaving, but could not bring himself to oppose the gentleman in Council.

Then Lord Dunmore, proud as any conquering hero, dismissed the Council and retired into the seclusion of his residence. But not for long. News arrived by messenger a-horseback, galloping madly and drawing up before the Palace gate with a suddenness that made the dust fly. Henry, the coward, afraid to ride to the Congress, was instead riding for Williamsburg with an army under his command. He was already at New Kent.

The Governor's bluster vanished. He forgot about laying his hands on Henry, and seemed anxious that Henry should not lay hands on himself. He ordered cannon dragged out and set about the Palace, he sent wife and children to take refuge on the *Fowey*, armed his Negro slaves and his Indian hostages, and by Lady Dunmore sent orders to Captain Montague, in command of the man-of-war, to dispatch a body of sailors and marines to protect him. Next he sent an urgent plea to the town authorities to call out the militia and march forth to stop Henry from reaching the capital. This was bluntly refused, and the Governor kept horses saddled, ready, with an escort, to flee to York and join his wife aboard the *Fowey*.

All along his march to Doncastle's Inn messenger after messenger had been sent by Williamsburg's important men, begging Patrick not to invest the town. Henry calmly gathered in the messengers and kept his way, and his silence. Arrived at the inn he found Ensign Goodall awaiting him, with the information that Corbin, the Receiver-General, had left for Williamsburg the day before Goodall had arrived.

The two men were still discussing this when lo! another messenger. This time it was Mr. Corbin's son-in-law, Carter Braxton, bringing not only the Governor's offer to pay the amount demanded for the powder, but the money itself.

This was announced to the little army, company by company. Was the offer satisfactory, and should it be accepted? Henry's opinion being asked, he replied that he so considered it. Upon which Mr. Braxton turned over the money and received the following receipt:

Doncastle's Ordinary, New Kent, May 4th, 1775. Received from the honourable Richard Corbin, Esq., his Majesty's Receiver-General, pounds 330, as a compensation for the Gunpowder lately taken out of the public Magazine by the Governor's order: which money I promise to convey to the Virginia Delegates at the General Congress, to be, at their direction, laid out in Gunpowder for the Colony's use, and stored as they shall direct until the next Colony Convention, or General Assembly, unless it shall be necessary in the meantime to use the same in defense of this Colony. It is agreed, in case the next Convention shall determine that any part of the said money ought to be returned to his Majesty's Receiver-General, that the same shall be done accordingly. Patrick Henry, Jr.

This settled, Henry sent a message to Robert Carter Nicholas, Treasurer of the Colony, to the effect that should it be deemed wise to transfer the public money to some place other than Williamsburg, he stood ready to provide a sufficient guard for that purpose. As to the affair of the powder, "that is now settled, so as to produce satisfaction to me, and I earnestly wish to the Colony in general."

From Mr. Nicholas came the immediate reply that there seemed no "necessity nor propriety for the offered service." Also news came that Williamsburg had quieted down and was no longer in fear of violence from the Governor. Whereupon Henry disbanded his men and everybody went home.

As soon as Dunmore was sure of this, courage and rage once again flamed in him. He issued one of his more furious proclamations against "Henry and his deluded followers . . . for their outrageous and rebellious behaviour," and their "extortion of three hundred and thirty pounds under pretence of replacing the Powder I thought proper to order from the Magazine, when it undeniably appears that there is no longer the least security for the life or the property of any man." He also warned that any person or persons found aiding and abetting the said P.H., would be in serious trouble, since his designs "would inevitably involve the whole Country in the most direful Calamity, as they will call for the vengeance of offended Majesty," and he ended nobly, "God Save the King, Dunmore."

There was a widespread feeling among the people that the Governor and the Council were in cahoots. Especially since the Council had issued a statement expressing "abhorrence and detestation of that licentious and ungovernable spirit that is gone forth, and misleads the once-happy people of this country." But if the Council was weak and spiritless, not so the people. A flood of congratulations, thanks, pledges of full support, poured in on Henry from all the country wide, and even after he set out to attend the Continental Congress in Philadelphia on May 11th, swift horsemen overtook him with these heartening messages. Before he left home, on May 9th, the County of Hanover adopted resolutions assuming full responsibility for all the actions he had taken, and thanking the Hanover Volunteers for their orderliness and good conduct, as also all those who had poured in from the different counties to march with them.

Henry set off, as a Hanover paper phrased it, "escorted by a number of respectable young gentlemen, Volunteers from this and King William and Caroline counties... who proceeded with him as far as Mrs. Hooe's Ferry, on the Potomac, by whom they were most kindly and hospitably entertained, and also provided with boats and hands to cross the river. After partaking of this lady's beneficence the bulk of the party took their leave of Mr. Henry, salooting him with two platoons and repeated huzzas. A guard accompanied the worthy gentleman to the Maryland side, to see him safely landed; and committing him to the gracious and wise Disposer of all human events, to guide and protect while contending for a restitution of our dearest rights and liberties, they wished him a safe journey and a happy return to his family and friends."

Although the paper did not mention it, this escort was not acting merely as an honor guard, but to make sure that Henry got safely out of Virginia, since it was common knowledge that Dunmore longed to capture and throw him into prison.

Most of the way Henry and Parke Goodall rode together. Henry talked freely to his friend of what he saw waiting in the future.

"War is coming, Parke, no doubt of that. The men of the North have begun it already, and they will not hesitate to go on with it. I pray that no cowardly reluctance will prevent us of the South from joining them; and I don't believe for a moment that it will. What I shall seek above everything is the union of all the colonies in a federation against England. This coming war, my friend, will be fought for complete independence. That will become the issue. But as yet the people as a whole are not ready to go so far. No, they're not quite ready yet, and for one, I don't believe in pressing them beyond their will. We must wait, we must watch, we must move forward wisely, not rashly. We are chosen by the people as their leaders, and lead we must; but not drive. There is a difference."

Henry took his seat in the Congress on May 18th, the day on which the news of the capture of Ticonderoga by Ethan Allen reached the members. Allen had captured large stores of ammunition, cannon, etc., and was sitting in triumph with his Connecticut and Massachusetts men. Startled, Congress justified him by the statement that the Captain's action was merely a measure of precaution, since it was known that armed British forces were on the way south from Canada to grab the stuff and proceed on with it to the attack of New York. Still keeping up the absurd pretense that there was no war on, Congress recommended that a careful inventory be made in order that all the captured stuff might be returned to Great Britain, "when the restoration of the former harmony between Great Britain and these colonies, so ardently wished for by the latter, shall render it prudent." There must have been a number of tongues in cheeks when that pious sentiment was passed.

But leaving the General Congress to move on from that point for the moment, we follow the concluding act of the Governor versus the Colony of Virginia.

Lord Dunmore called the General Assembly to meet at

the Capitol on June 1st, where he would give them a talk as to what was right and what was wrong. On the appointed day he did so, telling them that the state and behavior of many in the Colony was alarming, and that it was time for Virginia to accept the conciliatory measures offered her by the British Ministry, not only immediately, but with gratitude and devotion.

The Council made him the expected satisfactory response. The Burgesses were yet to speak when something happened, something that drove his lordship from the Palace to the *Fowey*, never to return.

After the stealing of the powder several citizens of Williamsburg had entered the Powder Horn to remove some firearms remaining there. When this was discovered Dunmore flew into one of his rages, screaming threats and insults. The older and more cautious men in the community recovered the arms and returned them to the Magazine, expressing their regret at the occurrence. But the Governor remained not only angry, but frightened, and hatched a mean and cruel revenge.

On June 5th a body of men, not at all content with the outcome in regard to these arms, gathered at the Horn to take the arms back. Two went ahead to open the door, followed closely by others. As the two pulled wide the door, a gun charged with swan shot and loaded almost to the muzzle, went off, wounding one of the men in the shoulder, while the second had a finger shot off and another so smashed it had to be amputated.

Cautious exploration revealed that spring-guns had been set up in various places in the Magazine, some of which could easily have killed an intruder. Also, several barrels of gunpowder were found buried in such a way that they would have been exploded by a rash entry.

Plain murder—that was what it could have been.

The smothered anger of the little city turned to white-hot fury, but there was no uprising that day. However, his lordship felt that he who runs away may be criticized but won't be harmed. Before dawn of the next day he with his wife and children, who had returned to the Palace, and Captain Foy, scooted for the *Fowey*, leaving a message addressed to the Speaker of the House of Burgesses saying he feared for his personal safety and that he would fix his abode aboard the ship where access to him was easy, and let there be no interruption in the sittings of the Assembly. If they had anything to say to him, one or two of the members, and not the whole House, could visit him at York, where the vessel lay.

Two members of the Council, with four Burgesses, went to see him. Lord Dunmore spent the time telling them to do everything they would not do and to obey all they would not obey, forbade them to touch the arms and cannon at the Palace, and refused to return to the capital to sign waiting bills. There was a long argument, as useless as long. So, assuring him, from the whole House, that they were sorry he had felt it necessary to run away when he was in no personal danger, and regretting the inconvenience Lady Dunmore and his children must be suffering, the deputation took its leave.

The Assembly, having received the report, agreed unanimously that there was no use continuing the argument, and adjourned until the following October. Last to leave the Capitol were Richard Henry Lee and two other Burgesses. The three stood chatting in the porch a few minutes, and then Lee, turning, pulled a pencil made in England from his pocket and wrote on one of the noble pillars the Witches' lines from Macbeth:

When shall we three meet again
In thunder, lightning, or in rain?
When the hurlyburly's done,
When the battle's lost and won!

The three men looked at each other in silence, with brooding in their eyes.

Chapter 14

SHADOW BOXING

WHEN Henry joined the Continental Congress in Philadelphia on May 18th the spirit of that body, led by John Jay and Dickinson, leaned toward appeasement. There must be another Petition to a scornful King. To be sure, New York was to protect herself from "insult and injury," when the British troops arrived in her harbor, but nothing rough, please—careful to act only in self-defense!

On the day he took his seat the note changed. A unanimous decision to arm the colonies was passed, New York was advised to fortify a post at Kingsbridge and another on the Highlands of the Hudson, to command the navigation of that river. This was the beginning of West Point.

The city was to defend itself stoutly, too—"as it is very uncertain whether the earnest endeavors of Congress to accommodate the unhappy differences between Great Britain and the Colonies will be successful." Henry's voice was certainly heard in those decisions. Other business of a warlike nature was completed: each colony was to look up possible sources from which lead could be obtained, and to start means to mine and prepare it. A cheap way of refining salt was another thing insisted upon as needing immediate attention. Henry was appointed to attend to these two items in Virginia, because people knew he got things done. And a postal service throughout the colonies was voted, with Benjamin Franklin as Postmaster General.

In June Boston was heard from. Let Congress immediately undertake the regulation and direction of the army investing that city.

On the 15th Washington was made Commander-in-Chief of American forces. Henry and Washington had been working together on several committees connected with military preparations and necessities. Both were satisfied that war was coming. After Washington had spoken his modest thanks for the great honor done him, he said to Patrick, and there were tears in his eyes, "This day will be the commencement of the decline in my reputation." But Henry, used to judging men, shook his head:

"On the contrary, from to-day it begins its true rise to greatness."

Henry was on many committees handling a vast deal of business, one matter close to his heart being the settling of the boundary dispute between Pennsylvania and Virginia. He got men from both colonies together and helped prepare an Address to the inhabitants of the disputed territory, recommending that, considering the importance of removing all obstacles to coöperation between the states, the armed men on both sides be disbanded, those under confinement or under bail be discharged, and that each person might be permitted to keep his property until the matter could be settled to the satisfaction of all. This Address was signed by nine of the most powerful men from both colonies, Henry's name leading. It served its purpose perfectly.

The Congress adjourned August 1st. It had been held this time in the State House, which became and remains to-day, *Independence Hall,* where the Liberty Bell hung. On the day before the adjournment there was a review of the Pennsylvania troops by Washington, light horse, artillery, rangers, riflemen, a colorful affair. All the members of Congress attended, the drums rolled, the fifes sounded, the sun shone, the streets were crowded with eager and cheering onlookers.

What William Cabell Rives called "Henry's striking and lucky *coup de main* in the gunpowder affair," was showing results.

After the adjournment every one went home. Edmund Pendleton, Benjamin Harrison, Patrick Henry, and Thomas Jefferson rode together to Richmond, where the Third Virginia Convention was already in progress. The fact that Henry and Jefferson were together on this journey from one city to the other gives one to think.

For Jefferson, speaking to Henry's biographer, Wirt, years after Henry's death, had told him, regarding this second Congress, the first for Jefferson:

I found Henry to be a silent and almost unmeddling member of Congress. On the original opening of that body, [the year before] while general grievances were the topic, he was in

his element and captivated all by his bold and splendid eloquence. But as soon as they came to specific matters, to sober
reasoning and solid argumentation, he had the good sense to
perceive that his declamation, however excellent in its proper
place, had no weight at all in such an assembly as that, of cool-
headed, reflecting, judicious men. He ceased therefore, in a
great measure, to take part in the business. He seemed, indeed,
very tired of the place and wonderfully relieved when, by appointment of the Virginia Convention to be Colonel of their
first regiment, he was permitted to leave Congress about the
last of July.

Interesting if true, to use an old phrase. Henry had been
more than a month at the Congress before Jefferson arrived, June 21. He was, until he left, after adjournment,
constantly at work in committees with men of "sober
reason and solid argument." He was not appointed Colonel
of the first, or another regiment, until the Virginia Convention did so, on August 5th, at Richmond, while he was
on his way there. Perhaps he looked, and felt tired. It is
the only possible bit of veracity in the sorry tale and it is
to be forgiven—he had been working hard, thinking hard.
Nor was it ever his habit to get up on the floor and talk
unless there were just cause. So much for that.

The Convention was almost entirely occupied with
military business. Henry found George Mason in the seat
beside his own, and the friendship already started was
strengthened. It lasted all of Mason's life and was a great
satisfaction to both men.

Before Henry's arrival and after considerable discussion
the Convention agreed to form a body of eight thousand
minute-men, and three regiments of regulars. But after
further argument they reduced the regular regiments to
two. It would be enough for the present, and the militia

would be available if more became necessary. Next had come the voting for officers.

On the first ballot Hugh Mercer, a Scottish doctor who had seen considerable service in the Indian wars, led. But it was very generally felt that Henry's name, with the Powder Horn incident fresh in all men's minds, would be a valuable drawing card for enlistments; he was moreover, those for him declared, a natural leader, and widely liked. So Patrick reached the Virginia Convention to find himself Colonel of the First Regiment, and Commander-in-Chief. William Woodford, an experienced soldier, was in command of the Second Regiment. He had fought hard for Mercer, having the professional's dislike for the amateur, and he resented Henry's appointment.

On August 26th, just before the Convention adjourned, Henry's commission was signed, and he gave his oath of loyalty. This Commission was signed by the newly formed Committee of Safety which Henry helped to create, and which would be the government of Virginia pro tem. For there was no regular government in the State yet. The Convention could not sit indefinitely; there was no governor. Therefore this Committee was created to carry on, which it usually did through a quorum; the chairman of the Committee and its quorum was none other than Pendleton. Henry's oath obligated him to carry out all orders and instructions the Committee issued. On his side, "all officers and soldiers and every person whatever, in any way concerned," were under Henry's command.

Since the Committee was not to meet until September 23rd of this year, 1775, Henry hastened home to Scotchtown.

His wife, Sally, had died some time before the adventure of the Powder Horn; she had long been ill of an incurable disease, and her death was a release from suffering, a release, as she had said to her husband, for which she prayed. His eldest daughter, Martha, married to John Fontaine, son of a family that had long been friends of the Henrys, took over the management of her father's house. Her husband had had military experience against the Indians, and was now a captain. He would soon leave for duty. There was much for Patrick to do to straighten his affairs, find a manager, prepare for a possibly long absence. He also wished to talk over military matters with his two brothers-in-law, William Christian and Samuel Meredith, both of whom would have commands in the new regiments.

West of the College, in the broad fields surrounding Williamsburg, a few days before the date for the meeting of the Committee, Henry pitched his tent, having been met outside the town and escorted onward by the entire body of volunteers, who, as the *Gazette* observed, "paid him every mark of respect and distinction in their power." Week by week the muster of new volunteers poured in until by mid-October nine full companies had been signed. Arms and uniforms were considerably rarer. Fowling pieces took the place of muskets, while the First Regiment wore hunting-shirts and leggings of buckskin, with blue breeches. Henry was clad like his men, with a three-cornered hat instead of a cap and a sword at his side to distinguish him.

The usual drilling, conferences, reception of new men filled the days. Also the struggle to get proper arms. There was an enemy to be attacked already, none other than Lord Dunmore, who was burning houses and villages along the coast, taking slaves, robbing right and left. One late October day, returning with Christian from a general review, Patrick expressed his concern.

"Why aren't we sent against that pirate, Will? How much longer is Pendleton going to keep us marking time here? I was talking with Page this morning, he says Pendleton appears reluctant to send armed forces against the ex-Governor, and that he asserts we aren't ready. But we are ready! We have enough men properly armed to oppose what forces Dunmore has. As for the Governor argument, when the House of Burgesses failed to meet last September, we all know that marked the end of British government here."

Only the quorum of the Committee was meeting, Pendleton its chairman, Carter Braxton hand and glove with him. George Mason, a stout aid to Patrick, was ill at home. John Page, Paul Carrington, Dudley Digges were other members. These were friendly to Henry, but Pendleton held the reins.

"The trouble lies with Pendleton, who hates you, and that son-in-law of his, Braxton, who's never forgiven you for forcing him to hand over the powder money," Will answered, ruefully. "And Pendleton's cock-of-the-walk. He wanted Woodford instead of you. Woodford's an old friend of his. They're near neighbors you know, with adjoining estates. He'll do his best to obstruct you, to keep you back."

Henry knew this was true. Still and all, the regiments were formed to fight, not sit around holding Pendleton's hand and waiting—waiting for what?

A day or two later the waiting ceased and Henry was given a direct slap in the face by the Committee. On October 26th a messenger came top-speed from Hampton, lying directly north of Norfolk across the broad stretch of water where the York flows into Chesapeake Bay. Captain Squire, commanding the British ship *Otter*, who had been doing a lot of destruction, had now threatened to burn the town unless certain leading men were surrendered, together with the public money. He had with him three tenders loaded with soldiers, and an armed sloop. There was a company of regulars in the town under Captain George Nicholas, and another company of minute-men. But they needed help.

Henry was ignored. Instead, Colonel Woodford was sent to the rescue with a small detachment of the Second Regiment and a company of riflemen. They reached Hampton after marching all night, at eight in the morning, found Squire just opening his attack, and joining with the men already there, drove the British back to their ships with a number of casualties, while the Virginians did not have a man scratched. This happy outcome was largely due to the rifle brigade under Captain Green, not one of whom ever drew a bead without hitting a man.

By one of those coincidences, this first fight between American and British armed forces in Virginia took place on the same ground where, a hundred and sixty years earlier, occurred the first encounter between Indians and the newly-arrived English.

Woodford had scarcely returned when Dunmore issued a furious proclamation declaring martial law throughout Virginia; calling every able-bodied man in the Colony to gather at once to his Majesty's standard or lose both life and property; announcing all Negroes belonging to rebels free if they joined him, adding all criminals for good measure. All this did not frighten the colonists, but it considerably annoyed them.

Henry at once asked the Committee to let him lead his

men to an attack on Norfolk, where the enemy was intrenched. He was again ignored, Woodford was ordered to the attack with his entire regiment and a detachment of Culpeper minute-men, and later eight hundred North Carolina men joined him. Adding insult to injury, on November 8th, following Dunmore's proclamation, the Committee sent Henry orders to prepare winter quarters for his troops.

Not even a show of obeying the provisions of Henry's commission was made. Woodford did not so much as communicate with his superior, as the commission required. When Henry demanded to know why he had received no dispatches to keep him informed of the course of events, Woodford, addressing him as "commanding officer of the troops at Williamsburg," coolly replied that he did not intend to communicate with him when he was sent "to command a separate and distinct body of troops under the immediate instructions of the Committee of Safety," adding that his duty was to address his intelligence to them "as the supreme power of this colony."

Woodford won the famous Battle of the Bridge over Dunmore with great loss to the English and hardly any to the Americans. It finished Dunmore, who after shelling Norfolk, disappeared with what plunder his ships could carry and troubled Virginia no more. Henry was generous enough to rejoice in this victory, but the winter was a bitter one for him.

When the Convention met again, December 1st, it rebuked Pendleton's actions by demoting him from first place on the Committee to fourth, and dropping Carter Braxton. But soon after it met, Colonel Howe, the commander of the forces from North Carolina who had joined Woodford, took command, with Woodford's assent,

of his regiment, too. So that the resolution passed by the
Convention to the effect that Colonel Woodford, even
though acting under a separate and detached command,
must correspond with Colonel Henry, and that, when
neither the Convention nor the Committee of Safety was
sitting, Woodford was subject to Henry's orders, became
academic. This was in answer to Henry's demand, laid
before them, to know whether or not he was the officer
in command.

The whole matter was an ugly, mean mess. And when
in February, Congress transferred the First and Second
Regiments to Continental service, appointing Colonel
Howe Brigadier General of both, as of other forces being
raised for such service, which meant Henry would be
demoted to being only the Colonel of the Second, he decided to take the way out, and resigned. He had not cared
to resign under Pendleton's persecution, but to the Congress, rearranging the whole military set-up, it was another
matter.

He must have done this with a feeling of tremendous
relief. He had accepted his commission with a high heart,
hoping to do his best and risk his life for the country he
loved, eager to become expert in his new position, to
learn from the friends and relatives already in the service
all they could teach, ready to lose his life on the field if
that should come, in the one great cause that had been his
blazing beacon ever since he was a man. Having done
much to bring on the fight for liberty, he wanted to serve
it on the field.

He had been given ashes for bread. They are bitter food.
Now he would put it all behind him, return, as many were
begging him to do, to membership in the Convention, and
work for his country in the legislature. There was much

to do, for a new nation was in the forming. Money, men, arms, ships, alliances—all must be found or created. Thank God there were more ways than one of serving liberty and your country.

Two days after Henry's resignation the *Gazette* carried the following information:

Yesterday morning the troops in this city being informed that Patrick Henry, Esq., resigned his commission the day preceding and was about to leave them, the whole went into mourning, and, under arms, waited for him at his lodgings, when they addressed him in the following manner (after a preliminary passage giving him their sincere thanks, as the only tribute it was in their power to give him, they concluded): "Notwithstanding your withdrawal from the service fills us with the most poignant sorrow, as it deprives us of our father and General, yet, as gentlemen, we are compelled to applaud your spirited resentment to the most glaring indignity. May your merit shine as conspicuous to the world in general as it hath done to us, and may Heaven shower its choicest blessings upon you."

Henry thanked them for their testimony of regard, and for the zeal and spirit they had constantly shown in their different stations, closing with these words:

"I am unhappy to part with you. I leave the service, but I leave my heart with you. May God bless you, and give you success and safety, and make you the glorious instruments of saving our country."

The officers of Henry's regiment had ordered a dinner in his honor at the Raleigh; immediately afterwards he intended starting for his home, spending the night en route (dinners in that time were always in the early afternoon) at a friend's home. The dinner was pleasant, Henry throwing aside any hint of gloom, and making his hosts laugh at some of the tales he had to tell of military doings. When the time came to leave, a number of them were to ride with him out of the town as a sort of good-by cortège. But when the party came out on Duke of Gloucester Street it found a number of soldiers, who, says the *Gazette,* were "behaving in a tumultous fashion." They greeted Henry's appearance with cheers and loud shouts announcing that they had come to get their discharge.

"If we can't serve under you, we'll not serve under any one, Sir. That we won't." Mad cheers greeted this.

Henry talked with those nearest him. He begged them to reconsider. There was the country to think of.

"I'll tell you what I want you to do, men. Go back to your barracks, and I'll visit you all, and we'll talk this thing over."

He turned to the officers near him, Lieutenant-Colonel Christian among them:

"I'll stay here to-night. We must persuade these men to give up their plan. You'll all help me."

So he went about from barrack to barrack, and backed by Christian and the rest, succeeded in inducing the soldiers to remain in the service.

"It would hurt me more to be the cause of your deserting our country in her need than anything else that can possibly happen," Henry told them. "I am going to do my best for the United Colonies, men, if not in the service, then out of it, in our halls of government. I trust you to do your best. That has been my aim since I was your commander; it is more so now than ever. Obey me this once more, and my thanks are yours forever."

In the end the soldiers, although reluctantly, yielded to his pleas. And the *Gazette* concluded its story of the event in these words:

We have the pleasure to assure the publick that those brave fellows are now pretty well reconciled, and will spend the last drop of their blood in the defence of their country.

Henry's own soldiers and the officers of the First Regiment were not the only ones to give him their sympathy. More than ninety officers, many of them under Woodford at Kemp's Landing and Suffolk, sent a round robin to the *Gazette*, asking to have it published, which was done. It was a fervent witness to the high esteem in which he was held, and which they desired to make public. Among much else these sentences are interesting, since they underline Henry's earlier work in bringing the desire for freedom to the Colony:

To your vigilance and judgment as a Senator, this United Continent bears ample testimony, while she prosecutes her steady opposition to those destructive Ministerial measures which your eloquence first pointed out, and your resolution led forward to resist. To your extensive popularity, also, the service is greatly indebted for the expedition with which the troops were raised, and while they were continued under your command, the firmness, candor and politeness which formed the complexion of your conduct towards them...will leave upon our minds the most grateful impression.

They had a solemn manner, those days, of expressing themselves, but their hearts were in the right place.

Patrick had hesitated at first on this matter of resigning his commission, but several men in the Convention, friends of his, strongly urged him to do so.

"You're needed in our councils. Affairs of the greatest importance to the future must be decided. As colonel of a regiment under superior officers you will be able to play but a small part in this future. Your place is with us, directing the formation of the government to be, lending all your genius to that end."

These were true words, and Henry saw it. He accepted them, and never again used the title of Colonel. That portion of his life was over, and good-by to it.

Chapter 15

THERE IS A TIDE IN THE AFFAIRS OF MEN

*I*T was March, 1776, when Henry drove home, free of the army and for the time free of politics. His youngest sister, Elizabeth, went with him. She had been in Williamsburg keeping house for her brother when he was away from the camp, and entertaining with him in the little cottage they had taken whenever he asked some of his officers to supper. Will Christian came often, so did his other brother-in-law, Sam Meredith, also a captain in Henry's regiment, and presently to be a colonel. Meredith brought a friend of his, another captain in the First, William Campbell, who instantly made himself liked. He was a striking-looking man, six feet two inches, with the blond hair and blue eyes of the Campbells and their fighting spirit. Straight and soldierly, courteous, with a charming chivalry toward women, a delightful humor, he had the quick, passionate temperament of the true Highlander. Elizabeth herself was a tall, slim, lovely young woman, with her brother's imagination and gift for wit. Before she left the two were engaged, and in June, 1777, they were married.

They made a handsome and lively pair and many a story was told of them. Once Campbell, who hated all Tories, came home to find one of them begging his wife to plead with the Colonel not to have him thrown into prison. Seeing him, Campbell, with a roar of rage, dashed toward him drawing his famous Andrea de Ferrara sword, an heirloom, and just as the man made a frantic leap through the door into the garden took a whack at his head which was deflected only because Elizabeth grabbed her husband's arm. The blow fell on the lintel, making a deep cut and slightly bending the point of the weapon, which could never be completely straightened.

Elizabeth showed it to Patrick one day, laughing.

"You have to be ready for anything with William, Pat, but really, I don't want even a Tory's head rolling loose in my drawing room!"

There was another adventure ending less happily for another Tory; he had been proved a spy, but got away. Coming out of church one Sunday Campbell saw the man riding a horse at a gallop across a side street. Instantly leaping on his own steed William put after him lickety-split. Seeing him, the Tory rode straight for the cliff above the river and leaped his horse into the water. After him went his foe, grabbed him, and managed to cling to him until others, who had seen the two, arrived.

When at last, drenched to the skin, he reached home, Elizabeth, who had come out of church with him, asked, "Did you catch him?"

"Yes, I caught him."

"What did you do with him?" she pursued.

"Oh, we hung him, Betty. That's all." And he went upstairs to change his clothes.

As the brother and sister drove homeward Henry remarked that one good thing had come of his being Commander-in-Chief.

"You have promised to marry a fine man, Betty. A man you might not have met otherwise."

And that was about the only allusion he ever made to his military experience, although once, having been asked what was the reason he had resigned from the Army, he answered laughing, "Why, I quit because I found it so cluttered with my relatives." Truth to tell, there were plenty of them.

It was not in his nature to remain bitter or resentful. He was not a man given to thinking of himself, and though for the moment he had come home to get a needed rest, he was already preparing for the future, for the tasks and opportunities it must, in such an era, hold in store.

Happily, Henry possessed to perfection the power of relaxation, although the thing itself was not preached nor considered for many and many a decade to come. During the next few weeks he went fishing and hunting with his sons, he visited his neighbors, the Dandridges among them, whose daughter Dorothea was a very charming and handsome young woman. Henry was forty years old this year, but retained his youthful appearance; tall, slender, with his slight stoop, his noble profile, his intensely blue eyes, he usually wore a dark wig, and here in the country dressed in hunting clothes with a cap, he looked to be in his early thirties. He and Dorothea went riding together as the spring mornings increased in beauty and mildness; he confessed to her that now the military experience was done with, he was glad to be back in the political life of the Colony.

"I suppose that I ought to have refused the nomination of Commander-in-Chief. Yet I imagine I'm not the only man with his country going to war, who yearns to be in the fight. But I'll have to be satisfied with verbal battle from now on."

"We're all glad you resigned. Father says you were abominably treated, but he also told us that he was happy to have you back where, as he said, you belong. He thinks there'll be a great deal to do in the coming session of the Convention—when is it to meet?"

"Early in May—the 6th, I believe. Yes, I'll feel at home in the Capitol again. We'll lay the foundations of government—our government—before we adjourn, if it takes a year."

"Our government?" she gave him a quick, flashing glance.

"Let it be a secret between us, but I think, I believe, that complete independence will be reached at this session."

"Father's promised to take me to Williamsburg when the Convention is sitting, and to see that I have a seat in the gallery when anything very exciting is forward. I hope I'm there when that happens."

"I hope you are."

Their eyes met, she colored, and lifting her bridle reins slightly, started her horse into a canter.

The Fifth, the last, and the most famous of the Virginia Conventions met in the Hall of the House of Burgesses in the Capitol on May 6, 1776. The place was crowded, many women besides Dorothea in the gallery, the hundred and twenty-eight delegates from the different colonies seated below on the ranged benches, tier above tier. Several were young, unused to the work but ready for it. Among these newcomers was Edmund Randolph, six feet tall—Virginians were generally tall men—twenty-five years old, distinguished-looking. He was the son of that John Randolph who had helped to pass Patrick Henry in his bar examinations.

But John was gone, fled to England, a Tory through and through. His son refused to accompany him, preferring his uncle Peyton's stand for freedom and democracy, and joined Washington at his camp. Now Peyton Randolph was dead, and young Edmund the only Randolph representing that great family in the legislature of his country—for the old custom of speaking of your colony as your country still held.

Young Randolph came as the alternate for George Wythe, who was sitting with the Congress in Philadelphia. He proved his heritage, and before the Convention adjourned it voted him his father's office of Attorney-General as a fit return for his loyalty. The young man was a fine speaker, clear and strong, and he knew where he was going. Another new man was James Madison, from Orange County, one of the few short men in the gathering. He, too, was just twenty-five, and but four years graduated from Princeton College. A pale, slender, delicate-looking young man, shy and quiet, but when he spoke revealing an excellent intelligence. In days to come he and Henry would oppose each other in debate, Henry asserting that he was perhaps the most formidable opponent he'd ever met.

Madison appeared, hatless and indignant, as the members gathered in the courtyard.

"Someone stole my hat," he exclaimed. "As fine a London conical as you ever saw—and doubtless the last I'll ever see! Taken right out of the hall of the house where I'm lodging. Some dashed Tory, I'll warrant." There was a general laugh, and Madison, suddenly shy again, slipped into the building.

Men were greeting each other; many crowded about Henry, shaking his hand, welcoming him back. Henry wore buckskin breeches, woolen stockings, a dark blue coat, his wig was unpowdered. Others were dressed in like style, but there were plenty who still wore fashionable silk or velvet, ruffles, powdered wigs. It gave a color and variety pleasant to the eye. Some of the delegates even wore swords, although this had long been out of fashion. But it was war time.

This was, of course, the first time the delegates to the Convention met in the Williamsburg Capitol, although a very large percentage of them had met there as Burgesses. In the canopied chair at the last session of the Assembly Peyton Randolph had sat. A new Speaker must now be voted. Edmund Pendleton was nominated by Richard Bland, very old and almost blind. He was seconded by Archibald Cary, a strong Pendleton man. Thomas Johnson, one of Henry's friends, rose to make a fiery protest, still seething with wrath over what Pendleton had done to Patrick. He proposed Thomas Ludwell Lee and was seconded by Bartholomew Dandridge, a relative of Henry's neighbor, Nathaniel, and brother-in-law to Washington. Pendleton won the appointment.

Henry took no part in this, and would have preferred not to have had the point raised. When later he was asked why he did not support Lee he said he believed it would have divided the Convention, and that to him the most important thing was to avoid all disunion.

"What we need and must have is a strong, united body which will get what needs to be done, done. I intend to work with Pendleton, not to stir up trouble."

And so he did, and "Henry's Party," as the men on his side were known, followed his leadership. There was a deal of work to be done before the matter of greatest importance could be touched. It was left discreetly alone until on May 14th, in the Committee of the Whole, Henry asked Thomas Nelson, who had supported him at St. John's Church, to introduce some "rough resolutions" in Henry's handwriting. These resolutions called for Independence, and no better man than Nelson could have been chosen to make the motion. He was no orator, but a fearless, straightforward speaker, a man who knew his own mind, and he had great influence.

There were three separate motions for independence, Henry's the first, Meriwether Smith's the second, Pendleton's the third. These so-called rough resolutions were discussed by the Committee of the Whole for two days, and in the end a kind of amalgamation of the three offerings was adopted. Each writer—their manuscript pages were found in the Capitol with other matter concerning the proceedings—first ran over the events and oppressive actions which had led the Colony to make the move toward independence, and then followed the *Resolve* each advised. Henry came out flat, as follows:

Resolved, That our Delegates in Congress be enjoined, in the strongest and most positive manner, to exert their ability in procuring an immediate, clear and full Declaration of Independence.

Smith had this to contribute:

Resolved, That the government of this colony as hitherto exercised under the crown of Great Britain be dissolved, and that a committee be appointed to prepare a Declaration of Rights, and such a Plan of Government as shall be judged most proper to maintain Peace and Order in this Colony, and secure substantial and equal liberty to the people.

Here is Pendleton:

Resolved, That the union that has hitherto subsisted between Great Britain and the American colonies is thereby totally dissolved, and that the inhabitants of this colony are discharged from any allegiance to the crown of Great Britain.

Henry, of course, spoke for his Resolution, and young Edmund Randolph says that only after he had explained that he offered it as what had seemed to him the one course for his country to take, and offered it only after patiently studying the feeling of the people on whom would fall the tremendous task of staking their lives and fortunes on the issue, did he swing into the full magnificence of his genius. "He entered into no subtlety of reasoning, but was aroused by the now apparent spirit of the people. As a pillar of fire, which nothwithstanding the darkness of the prospect would conduct to the promised land, he inflamed and was followed by the convention. His eloquence unlocked the secret springs of the human heart, robbed danger of all its terror, and broke the keystone in the arch of royal power."

In fact, he was in good form and high spirits. It is a pity that the Committee did not adopt his simple, powerful *Resolve* just as it stood. But as usual they had to drag in a lot of unnecessary words, so much the habit of the political mind. Perhaps, since it was presented to the Congress in

Philadelphia, we had best read it, particularly since it was
the first in the country to order its delegates to demand
Independence. Again, in the last, as in the first act leading
to freedom, Virginia carried the banner, and again, as
before, Patrick Henry was the man who placed it in her
grasp. Skipping the wordy Preamble, here is the Resolution:

Resolved, unanimously, That the Delegates appointed to
represent this colony in General Congress, be instructed to
propose to that respectable body to declare the United Colonies free and independent states, absolved from all allegiance
to, or dependence upon, the crown or parliament of Great
Britain, and that they give the assent of this colony to such
declaration, and to whatever measures may be thought proper
and necessary by the Congress for forming foreign alliances
and a confederation of the colonies... Provided that the power
of forming government for and the regulations of the internal
concerns of each colony, be left to the respective colonial legis-
latures.

Resolved, unanimously, That a committee be appointed to
prepare a Declaration of Rights and such a plan of government
as will be most likely to maintain peace and order in this colony, and secure substantial and equal liberty to the people.

The same day these resolutions were passed, May 15th,
General Nelson started with them post haste for Philadelphia and the Congress. The British flag was hauled
down from over the dome of the Capitol and the Union
flag hauled up to fly proudly against the sky, while the
soldiers paraded, the cheering populace lining the broad
street. At night the town was illuminated, cannon roaring
at sunset, the Raleigh and every other inn crowded with
toast-drinking gentlemen. Next day a number of the
wealthy contributed to a grand picnic for the soldiers, held
in one of the parks. And after that every one settled down
to the business of preparing for the future.

It is interesting to note that before the Convention met Henry had been dubious as to the wisdom of demanding a declaration of independence. He felt that it was necessary to have the people strongly behind such a move, and he also believed it would be better first to test out the possibility of foreign alliances. He felt that ambassadors should visit France, to head off British attempts to secure her assistance.

"The half of our continent offered to France by Britain," he wrote his friend John Adams, "may induce her to aid our destruction... I know the free trade with all the States we mean to offer would be more beneficial to her than any territorial possessions she might acquire... yet, pressed, allured as she will be—but above all ignorant of the great things we mean to offer, may we not lose her?"

Richard Henry Lee, on April 20th, from Philadelphia, wrote him a long letter upholding the immediate necessity of ending dependence on Britain. He knew Henry was heart and soul of his own opinion that independence was the only outcome, but Lee saw no sense in delaying it. Virginia, he believed, was being watched anxiously by the other colonies; she had always taken the lead, she must take it now. He admitted that every maritime state in Europe was being interceded for to send no help of any kind to America, and that several had been applied to for troops to fight in the colonies. But he was certain that no "State in Europe will either Treat or Trade with us so long as we consider ourselves Subjects of Great Britain." And Shakespeare-loving Lee ended a splendid letter with these lines and a strong plea:

"There is a Tide in the Affairs of Men
Which, taken at the Flood, leads on to
Fortune—

"Let us therefore, quitting every other consideration, heartily unite," in declaring for independence, though it must lead to war.

John Adams wrote in the same vein, and other men gave witness that the people were ready for the inevitable declaration. Among these was General Charles Lee, just appointed to the command of the Southern Department. On arriving at Williamsburg before the Convention assembled, Henry met this gentleman, a spirited soul who was all for immediate action, and had a talk with him, followed next day by a letter, making it clear the General was sure the people were on the right side. "The military, in particular, are outrageous on the subject," declared the General, "and a man of your excellent discernment need not be told how dangerous it would be in our present circumstances, to dally with the spirit or disappoint the expectation of the bulk of the people."

General Lee, somewhat earlier, had written (the two men were not related) to Richard Henry Lee, soon after the Congress had met, the following amusing and forthright expression of opinion:

Pendleton is certainly a man of sense, but I can assure you that the other night, in a conversation I had with him on the subject of independence, he talked, or rather stammered nonsense that would have disgraced the lips of an old midwife drunk with bohea-tea and gin...For God's sake, why do you dawdle in the Congress so strangely—why do you not at once declare yourself a separate, independent State?

Yet this brave-spoken man would, later, dishonor himself as patriot and soldier.

Now all the hesitations and trepidations were over. Newspapers and individuals the country over applauded Virginia's action, although it took some time for the

Congress to arrive at practical unanimity. At last, June 7th, Richard Henry Lee moved, "That these united colonies are and of right ought to be, free and independent States." On July second all the colonies except New York voted for it, New York joining on the 9th.

In the meanwhile Thomas Jefferson had written his Declaration of Independence, and July 4th, 1776, had taken its place with the other great days of history in the ranks of the Immortals.

Meanwhile, in Virginia, the Convention was deep in the task of creating a State Government.

Chapter 16

THE FIRST AMERICAN GOVERNOR

ON May 15th, 1776, Virginia set to work to form the plan and work out the details of her government. On June 28th the job was finished and finished so well that it remained the fundamental law of Virginia for the next fifty-four years.

A committee was appointed by the Convention to perform the task. There were thirty-two members, among whom George Mason, Patrick Henry, Thomas Ludwell Lee, brother of Richard Henry Lee, and James Madison, were the men who did the work. Mason had brought with him a draft of the bill he intended to present, which he showed to Henry, who had also set down certain points, with some suggested by John Adams. Mason adopted several of these before writing out the Declaration to present to the Committee.

"We can expect," he told Henry, "a thousand ridiculous, impractical suggestions, with plans formed of jarring and unintelligible ingredients. We can only prevent this by bringing together a few men of integrity and ability whose country's interest lies next their hearts, who will undertake the business and defend it through every stage of opposition."

This was what Henry had feared, this bungling by a lot of men who did not measure up to the "business." He had so written to John Adams, wishing he and "your Sam" could have been with him. Now he knew Mason was as good or better.

When Mason presented his paper for the Bill of Rights and Plan of Government a number of other projects drifted out of sight. There were some hot disputes, certainly, as article by article was debated. Thomas Ludwell Lee, writing his brother, comments thus upon some of it:

I will tell you plainly that a certain set of Aristocrats—for we have such monsters here—finding that their execrable system cannot be reared on such foundations, have to this time kept us at bay on the first line, which declares all men to be born free and equal. All number of absurd or unmeaning alterations have been proposed. The words as they stand are approved by a very great majority, yet by a thousand masterly fetches and stratagems the business has been so delayed that the first clause stands yet unassented to...

In the end, and with only few alterations, "some of which I think not for the better," as Mason wrote his cousin, George Mercer, the Bill of Rights was passed, June 12th. Then came the establishing of the Plan, the order and details of the government. Henry put in a good piece of work here when he fought for the Governor's power of veto. Young Edmund Randolph, who attended every meeting, set down in his notes: "No member but Henry could with impunity to his popularity, have contended as strenuously as he did for an executive veto on the acts of the two houses of legislature."

Mason's plan had not given the governor any voice at all in the enactment of the laws. Truth was that the colonists' hatred for any sort of "kingly" prerogative was so bitter they wanted nothing remotely resembling it vested in any man. But Henry won his point with one of his fine and ardent speeches. Without the power of veto, the governor, he convinced his hearers, would be "a mere phantom... a dependent, instead of a coördinate branch of power."

The Committee of the Whole presented the results of its debating on June 28th in Philadelphia. They were adopted unanimously next day. A *Preamble* written by Jefferson was used as prefix to the document. Then came the business of electing a governor and appointing his council. Three men were nominated. Henry, by the democratic element; the aged Thomas Nelson, Sr., by the old time aristocratic group, and John Page by some one who must have cast the solitary vote he received. Henry won with sixty votes over forty-five for Nelson. The Council elected consisted of John Page, Dudley Digges, John Taylor, John Blair, Charles Carter of Shirley, Benjamin Harrison of Berkeley, Bartholomew Dandridge, and Thomas Nelson, Sr. But Mr. Nelson refused, in a huff over losing the governorship, giving "age and infirmities" as his excuse. Evidently he felt an aged and infirm Governor would have been all right.

Pendleton had voted for Nelson, and when Spencer Roane asked him why he hadn't himself been a candidate, replied that it was because he didn't think "it becomes those who pushed on the revolution to get into the first offices." Nelson had certainly not "pushed on the revolution," but, for that matter, had Mr. Pendleton?

Roane, who saw the dig at Henry, replied cheerfully:

"A nice figure we'd have cut if we'd given the office to a man who isn't even a Whig, as I understand is the case in regard to Mr. Nelson, wouldn't we?"

But Mr. Pendleton couldn't find the answer to that one.

So here stood Virginia, on June 29, 1776, having declared her independence, written her constitution, made her plan of government, elected her governor and her council three days before July 2d, when Congress took its final vote on the question of independence. Something of a record, and quite in line with her past!

George Mason, who had nominated Henry as Governor, waited upon him with the committee come to announce his election. That evening the small group who had really created the new government had supper together at the Raleigh as guests of Mason. They teased Henry, who plainly said he was alarmed at the prospect of running affairs—even with the Council to save him.

"I wonder what Dunmore would say if he knew you were in *his* Palace, at *his* desk, doing *his* job," remarked Tom Lee.

"The Raleigh's stoutly built of brick and stone, Tom," Henry answered, "but I wouldn't be surprised to see it fly apart under such an assault. We've heard him in some of his tempests—it might be interesting if he should stroll in on us now."

Not only from his own State but from all over the

"I wonder what Dunmore would say if he knew you were
in *his* Palace, at *his* desk, doing *his* job. ..."

country came letters of congratulation to Henry, felici-
tating Virginia on her choice. And, highly appreciated,
the officers of the two regiments over which he had been
appointed Commander-in-Chief sent him a round robin
expressing their delight in this recognition of his "worth
and genius." The only name not on the roster was Colonel
Woodford's, which gave Henry a moment's amusement.

On July 5th, 1776, the first American Governor and his
Council in all the land, took the oath of office.

Under the new constitution the Assembly consisted of
two branches, the Senate, elected by the people, and a
House of Delegates, members of the late Convention. The
Governor's term was for one year, and he was eligible for
reëlection twice in succession. After that a new Governor
must be chosen, and serve at least a year before his
predecessor could again be returned to the office.

Everything properly arranged, the Assembly adjourned
until the coming October. The Governor and his Privy
Council, of whom John Page was president, carried on the
governing meanwhile. For the whole three years to come,
Henry being reëlected without opposition or an opposing
candidate at the end of each of his terms, the chief job was
a bitter, unceasing struggle to raise troops, thousands for
Continental service, other thousands for home defense; to
find money; to defend the western border from Indian
attacks, where Colonel Christian did splendid work; to
provide food, clothes, shoes to Washington's ragged and
starving forces. On December 20, 1776, the *Gazette* printed
heartbreaking news. Washington's retreat across New Jersey, the fleeing from Philadelphia to Baltimore of the
Congress. General Charles Lee commanded half of the
Army on that occasion, and had disobeyed Washington's

orders to join him, leaving his superior to his fate. To be sure, two weeks later the *Gazette* came out with the heartening account of Washington's magnificent stroke in crossing the Delaware, beating the Hessians, and taking a thousand prisoners, on December 26th, followed on January 3d by the victory of Princeton. Cornwallis, all set to return to England in glory, with the colonies in his pocket, had to scramble off the vessel he had boarded and return to the fray—return to the long succession of near victories that ended, one summer day a little more than four years later, in the surrender of his sword to his despised but victorious foe, on the battlefield near enough to Williamsburg for the voices of the cannon to be heard in her streets.

In this same grim December of Henry's first year as Governor the alarmed Assembly voted an increase in the powers of the Governor, with only slight opposition, as it was recognized that the Governor must be free to take swift action if necessary. This has since been done in all times of great stress and danger. The Senate changed one line in the Act to read "Additional powers to be given the Governor and Council for a limited time," instead of "The usual forms of government shall be suspended for a limited time."

Some of Henry's enemies tried to make out that the Governor was attempting to grasp dictatorial power, and one of them, Archibald Cary, stout ally of Edmund Pendleton, meeting Henry's stepbrother, Colonel Syme, on Duke of Gloucester Street, rushed at him in an hysterical rage, shouting, "I'm told your brother wants to be dictator. Tell him that the day of his appointment shall be the day of his death—for he shall feel my dagger in his heart before the sunset of that day!" Hoop-la! Colonel Syme, a quiet and controlled person, stared at the frothing Cary a moment, then, remarking that if any such project existed certainly his brother knew nothing of it, and that any office "even in the most distant manner endangering the liberties of the country would be utterly foreign to him," walked off. All Williamsburg was laughing over that before the day was over. Certainly at the time the incident attracted no serious attention, yet five years later Jefferson, then furious at Henry, in writing his *Notes on Virginia* insinuates that Henry was behind a scheme "to create a Dictator, invested with every power, legislative, executive, judiciary, civil and military over our persons and our properties, [and] that a considerable portion of the House meditated a surrender of them into a single hand." And whose but Henry's? Jefferson was not in Williamsburg at the time of this dire attempt, and the Journal of the Assembly contains nothing to sustain his accusation. Moreover, he continued to uphold Henry as Governor, and himself renominated him in 1778. Also, greater powers were voted Jefferson when he became Governor, without appearing to alarm him.

In August, 1776, Patrick had been taken ill and went home for three weeks by his doctor's orders. During that time Colonel George Rogers Clark, of the Kentucky militia, and the most influential man in that western portion of Virginia's territory, turned up in Williamsburg. He came to ask the gift and conveyance of five hundred pounds of powder, which he must have to defend the western border. The Council, to which he appealed, hesitated. Clark at once left for Scotchtown to see Henry. The two men had never met before. They had a long talk. Clark was a Virginian, born in Albemarle County, and he believed that Kentucky was vital to the whole defense of western Virginia, and so did Henry.

"The Indians are up, urged on by the British. I've got men, good men, and arms, but we're damned short of gunpowder. Can I get it from you?"

Patrick thought he both should and could. He gave him a letter saying so, to be handed to the Council, and to Clark he had said, "Just insist!"

Clark found the Council still hesitating. He was told he must see to the conveying himself. And should the Assembly later disapprove of the transaction, he must hold himself answerable for it.

The Colonel turned on his heel, remarking:

"Very well, Sirs. If you aren't willing to defend a country, you have no right to claim it. I know others will not hesitate to give me what I ask, and Kentucky will consider herself free to make what future arrangements she thinks best."

Upon which the Council had a change of heart—and mind. Clark got all he asked for. The result was the saving of Kentucky to Virginia.

When, June 5th, 1777, Henry was notified of his reëlection, he took a vacation, not being required to give his oath of office before July 2nd. He wanted to be home for the marriage of sister Elizabeth; indeed, had promised to act as best man. Also his temperamental uncle, the Reverend Patrick, had died suddenly a few weeks earlier and left Henry to be his executor. As many of the family as could manage it arrived at Scotchtown to help celebrate the wedding; it was a joyful affair and a great relief from the pressing work of the governorship. It was on this occasion, when one of the guests asked Henry why he had resigned from the army, that he laughed, giving the answer.

"To tell you the truth I found it too cluttered with my relatives," nodding toward the group around Elizabeth. Patrick had five brothers-in-law, besides his own brother and his half-brother all of whom were colonels, while his daughter Martha's husband was a major. Not quite all had been able to come to the wedding, but the guest caught the point of the joke.

Before the Governor went back to Williamsburg her parents announced Dorothea Dandridge's engagement to him. The marriage would take place in October.

Dorothea was nineteen years younger than the man she was to marry, but the union was in every way a success. He made her his confidante in his political problems, trusted her judgment. They were true friends and mates as well as lovers. Dorothea was to bear him seven sons and six daughters, yet keep her beauty and her gaiety of spirit. An exquisite hostess, she presided over his home with charm and ease. One of six sisters, daughter of a rich family, she had been in close contact since girlhood with the best of Virginia's society. Her uncle John Dandridge was Washington's brother-in-law, and on her mother's side her great-grandfather had been Virginia's finest royal governor, Alexander Spottswood. In addition, she had Henry's love for the wilderness country and was a firstrate horse-woman.

Henry went back to his desk at the Palace. There was a tough year ahead, ending with the dreadful winter of Valley Forge. Washington wrote fully to Henry of the increasing peril of the situation, of the miserable ineffi-ciency of Congress, whose worthless quartermaster and commissary departments were the chief cause of the rags and starvation his army had to endure. The Governor de-voted himself with a burning fury to increasing the help

Virginia could give. He even kicked out the man Congress had appointed as the State's purchasing agent, John Moore, writing Richard Henry Lee, "I am really shocked at the management of Congress in this department... Good God, our fate committed to a man utterly unable to perform the task assigned him! Raw, inexperienced, without weight, consequence or acquaintance with men of business, called into action at a time when distinguished talent alone can save the army from perishing." The man he appointed in Moore's place, John Hawkins, accepted the task of straightening out the mess only because he was Henry's good friend. Although he was to die a few months later, he had brought about in that brief period so great a change that Jefferson wrote Henry (this was of course before he became Henry's enemy), "I am mistaken if, for the bodily subsistence of the troops hitherto we are not principally indebted to the genius and exertions of Hawkins, during the very short time he lived after his appointment to that department by your board."

Henry had also written a stiff rebuke to Congress for its whole miserable mismanagement, "a mismanagement from which have flowed evils threatening the existence of American liberty."

At the beginning of October Patrick married, bringing his bride to the Palace. There was no time for a honeymoon, but there was a piece of military good news, the victory over Burgoyne at Saratoga on the 17th of that month. This, in which the Virginian Colonel Dan Morgan bore a great part with his sharp-shooters, was later found to be a turning point in the war. Henry showed how deep was his feeling that America was one country in another letter to Lee, saying: "I rejoice at the success over Burgoyne, and I rejoice because the New England men had so great a share in it. For a malevolent set are continually endeavoring to spread jealousys of these, our honest, best and most faithful allys... I hope now we shall hear no more to their prejudice."

December brought the year to an end with one interesting event: the reappearance of George Rogers Clark with a plan, and a big one.

The British Governor of Detroit, Henry Hamilton, disrespectfully known as the Hair Buying General because he paid every Indian for bringing in an American scalp, was arming the red men, and threatening the western border of Kentucky and farther north.

"What must be done, Governor, is to end the menace of the chain of forts that stretch from the Mississippi to Lake Huron, from Detroit to Kaskaskia. I can raise the men, but must have money to pay and to arm them. That you'll have to do, but I assure you, the defense of Virginia begins at Detroit."

He had his scheme of operation carefully worked out. It must be secret, and it was sound. Henry sent the Assembly a special message asking for the necessary funds, and Clark left on what was to prove a greatly successful campaign.

On May 29, 1778, Henry was reëlected as before, Jefferson, who had nominated him, being the chairman of the committee who waited on Henry, as was customary, to inform him of the fact. Also, as was customary, Henry wore black small clothes, a scarlet cloak, and a powdered wig to receive the visitors and to voice his heartfelt appreciation. The early part of the year had brought the splendid news that the treaty of France had been signed, February 6, to be ratified May 4th. This was a high satisfaction to

Henry, who had from the first insisted that France should join in the struggle with Virginia. In July came the first French Minister, arriving with the French fleet under d'Estaing. The British army under General Sir Henry Clinton, alarmed at the news of the sailing, decided to abandon Philadelphia and return to New York. Washington followed them at once, giving General Charles Lee directions to meet the foe at Monmouth on their way to Sandy Hook, where Washington would join him and they could perhaps chop the British up. Lee, after deserting Washington on the retreat through New Jersey, had been captured by the British, but had been exchanged and was again in command of one-half of Washington's forces.

But Lee avoided the encounter, leading his men, in wild disorder, pursued by a part of Clinton's force, to meet the advancing Washington. There was a mad mix-up when the meeting occurred, and Washington, galloping straight up to Lee, shouted "What's the meaning of this?" Lee muttered some incoherent reply, and glaring at him with blazing contempt, the General ordered "Get to the rear, Sir!"

The retreat was checked, but the plan to catch the enemy between the two arms of the American Army was lost. Some months later Lee was dismissed in disgrace from the army. Later still proof came that he had sold himself to the British. Lee had wit, charm, spirit, but no honor. When, at the time Washington was made Commander-in-Chief, Lee had been appointed Major-General, he did not accept until assured that in case his estate was damaged he should be paid in full for all losses. This attitude was rather a smack in the face for both Washington and Henry, who had backed him for the position since he had borne an excellent record as a fighting officer before coming to America.

At the end of Patrick's last year as Governor his State was attacked by a fleet of over thirty British ships, large and small, bringing a landing force of eighteen hundred men. On May 8th, 1779, they sailed between the Capes and up along the coast, burning and cannonading. Terrific damage was done before they were stopped, for though Patrick was warned by his outposts as soon as the ships were sighted, it took ten days to raise three or four thousand troops and five more of stiff fighting before the enemy was cleaned out.

But there was also a piece of good news. Clark sent an escort with information that he had captured the forts and was threatening Detroit. With the report came a bunch of prisoners, the Hair Buying General among them, who was put into Williamsburg's "strong sweet prison."

An attempt to have Henry reëlected for a fourth term was headed off when he sent in his resignation a few days before the election was due. It was claimed that there was a very general desire throughout the State to have him continue, and furthermore that since the Convention of 1776 and not the Assembly (that body not itself elected at the time) had voted him in, the first election need not be counted. Henry would have nothing of such a quibble, and on May 28, 1799, headed the committee of information, thus returning the compliment Jefferson had paid him the year before, to welcome Thomas Jefferson as second Governor of Virginia. Jefferson had squeezed in with sixty-seven votes over sixty-two for John Page. Page was doomed never to be Governor of Virginia.

Henry took his leave of Williamsburg with the satisfaction of knowing that so far as the Commissariat went,

Washington was in the clear. In February Baron von Steuben had arrived and been appointed his Inspector-General, getting to work at once training and disciplining the troops, while General Nathanael Greene became Quarter-Master General. With these two splendid men and some sharp changes in the Congressional set-up Washington's troubles in that direction were over. At last the soldiers would be well-trained, properly fed and clothed.

Chapter 17

FAR FROM THE MADDING CROWD

WHEN June arrived it found Patrick and his family leaving Richmond for a new home. Scotchtown had been sold and at a good profit. Both he and Dolly were heartily tired of the crowded life they had been living, and Henry had been suffering for several weeks with a return of the old trouble, malaria. His wife was worried. Couldn't they get into the hills, far away from the malaria-stricken coast? Patrick jumped at the idea. He had heard that the owner of Leatherwood, a large estate on the creek of that name in Henry County, wanted to sell. He bought it.

This county had been set off in 1776 from the great border county Pittsylvania to honor Patrick, and in 1791 the section adjoining it to the west was given his first name.

So the two greatest orators of their day met in the tumbling hills and wild forests watered by wilder streams of that lovely part of the State, to remain side by side for all time.

One of Henry's elder sons had gone over Leatherwood thoroughly for his father before the purchase was made and brought him a careful description of both the house and the country.

"It's good land, and the house stands high close to the creek. You can hear its song as it runs by. There's plenty of game, Father, and a glorious view westward up the slopes of the Ridge to the Pinnacles, that seem fairly to scrape the sky. It's wild, but the turnpike between Wytheville and Danville is in easy reach. You and Mother will love it; the air's so dry and bracing, just what you need." He was enthusiastic, and Patrick laughed at him.

"I can see you mean to visit us whenever you can leave your own farm, Bill. You'll be welcome."

"Wait till you see the Falls of the Dan, and the deer coming to drink at the creek. They'll beat my words."

That was in May. Henry paid Thomas Lomax for the ten thousand acres and the house five thousand pounds. Three thousand pounds were paid at once in tobacco notes, worth more than twice the depreciated currency of that day, the money being raised by the sale of lands Patrick owned in Botetourt County and in Kentucky. Before the end of the year the last shilling due was paid, December 1, 1779, and Lomax was more than satisfied. The records remain and cannot be doubted.

But Jefferson, who could not have been aware when he spoke that this was the case, told Wirt that the purchase "was on long credit and finally paid in depreciated paper not worth oakleaves." Jefferson's word is worth less. One can but marvel that, even granting that he wanted to discredit Henry, he would make slanderous statements in regard to affairs of which he knew nothing. But so it was.

One hundred and ninety-two miles stretched from Richmond to Leatherwood, and a joyful cavalcade set off in the style of that day. Colonel Fontaine, invalided from the army, and daughter Martha, with their children, were to settle with the Henrys, and when he was away, as he knew he must be, there would be his son-in-law to head the family and manage the place. Then there was Dorothea's year-old daughter, little Dorothea Spottswood Henry. Patrick's two unmarried daughters, girls in their teens, with their youngest brother, children of his first marriage, were along. There were carriages, riding horses, and wagons loaded with household stuff. There were the slaves, male and female, and their children. At the end came the cattle and farm horses, mules, sheep. Moving in that time was something worth doing!

Although Henry had a bad attack of malaria after reaching Leatherwood, during the summer, the bracing weather of autumn put him on his feet again. Presently he was hunting and fishing. Dorothea was expecting her second child at the end of the year, but was in fine health. She was planning her flower garden with her old gardener, who had been given to her by her parents. Once, when her husband asked, "Do you truly like it here, Dolly?" she answered, "Oh, Pat, I hope we stay here the rest of our lives!"

Early in October Patrick received news of his election to the Congress, due to meet again in Philadelphia with the coming of November. The letter had been sent after the election, June 1st, and had been coming ever since.

When Henry wrote back declining the nomination he explained the delay in his reply, adding that he was sending two letters in case one miscarried. Not only did he wish to stay at home and guard his barely recovered health, but he wanted to be with Dolly when the child was born. This happened on January 4, 1780, another girl, whom they named Sarah Butler.

The year that had passed saw the war swing south as far as Georgia, though there was little action, Washington sitting with an eye on Clinton, who was snugly established in New York, where he was awaiting reinforcements. At the end of the year he got them in large number and immediately sailed for Charleston, North Carolina, where General Lincoln was in command of the American force, chiefly Virginians. Clinton swamped him with both men and cannon. Hoping for reinforcements Lincoln hung on until May 12, 1780, before surrendering his army, and all the ships in the harbor, together with much valuable military and naval material. A sickening blow to the country.

While the siege was still on Jefferson wrote Henry in February urging him to return to the Legislature, and when the Assembly met, May 1st, Henry was back in Williamsburg, hoping the climate would not get him down. He remained through the month, and was made chairman of the important Ways and Means Committee, whose greatest struggle was concerned with the terrible inflation of the currency. The paper money issued by Congress had fallen to one-fortieth of its printed value. Henry wanted a pay-as-you-go system instituted, even though it called for all the taxes the people could bear, supporting and carrying his proposal in a triumphant speech by a vote of 59 to 25. That done, and with only minor matters to settle and the Assembly due to adjourn shortly, Patrick went home. After he had gone, however, the tax bill was brought up again, defeated, and the proposal of Congress adopted. The people, it was argued, like all people, didn't want to be taxed and Congress's plan, although confused, might work. Henry had warned it would mean increasing inflation and was right. Within a year the paper had fallen to five hundred to one, and was worthless. You can't be kind to money.

Back to Leatherwood was like getting back to the Promised Land. The gentle yet steady routine of home and estate, the children, the fishing with his boys and riding with Dolly. But back of its peace and beauty the war went on. On August 16th came the sinister news of the Battle of Camden in South Carolina, when the American Army under Gates was almost annihilated by Cornwallis. De Kalb, that great soldier, did his best in vain to persuade Gates to use sounder tactics. But Gates was vain and conceited—he had been one of the group known as the Conway cabal, formed in 1778 to oust Washington from the command and put in his place "a Gates, a Lee (Charles), a Conway." The group contained a good many men, a Dr. Rush among them, who wrote Henry an anonymous letter trying to draw him into the conspiracy. Henry sent the letter to Washington, and Washington never forgot it. Rush always professed a great friendship for George, to whom he had written often, and George recognized his handwriting—thus aiding in the cabal bust-up. This same Gates had recently been given the command of the Southern Army by a foolish Congress, and now he threw the battle away, was himself the first to flee, running ahead of his disordered and routed men, reaching Charlotte, North Carolina, sixty miles away, in less than twenty-four hours. De Kalb stayed with the brave Continentals and died on the field. In November Congress at last removed Gates from the command, Washington appointing the brilliant, resourceful and, after much careful work, triumphant General Nathanael Greene in his place.

Fortunately the good came after the bad. On October 6-7 Colonel William Campbell, Henry's brilliant and Tory-hating brother-in-law, led the famous attack against the British Captain Ferguson up Kings Mountain, just on the North Carolina side of the border between herself and her sister to the south. Colonel Shelby, North Carolinian, was with him, a great Indian fighter. Campbell was especially eager because Ferguson was not only a top-flight officer but because he had many Tories in his command.

When the fighting was over Ferguson lay dead on the mountain's crest, all his men either killed or captured. Few Americans were lost, the whole affair having been handled with perfect planning, great ability, and a complete understanding between men and officers.

The news reached Richmond, where Henry arrived for the new convention of the Assembly on October 16, a short time later. Richmond had been chosen because there were fears of possible invasion by sea, and Williamsburg was too exposed. Campbell's victory was a great heartener after a hard year for America. Henry managed to see Elizabeth and bring her some details of her husband's success. She was delighted but not surprised. "So like William, Pat. He must have enjoyed himself." Pat grinned. Betty was a girl after his own heart.

The members of the Assembly were slow to come together, a quorum not being achieved until November 6th. Two days later Washington wrote Governor Jefferson that a British fleet was gathering and that he had almost certain information that it was headed for Virginia. Jefferson did nothing at all, and on December 9th Washington repeated the warning, sending a circular letter to the governors of all the southern seacoast states, warning them to prepare. Still Jefferson remained inert, until, on December 30th, General Thomas Nelson sent him a dispatch saying that a British fleet had sailed into Chesapeake Bay. The communication reached Jefferson next day, and he sent back permission to raise the militia of the lower part of the country, intimating that he was by no means certain the fleet was the enemy's. The Assembly adjourned on January 1st, having spent almost the whole of the session trying to settle, with no success, the endless disputes in regard to the Northwestern Territory which were seething between the states. On the 2nd, almost two months after Washington's first dispatch, Jefferson, having received fresh and urgent messages, decided that the ships must be British, after all, and sent out a requisition to the counties most threatened to raise forty-five hundred men. Nelson so far had only been able to get hold of a few hundreds. Three days later Benedict Arnold, traitor since the end of September, burned Richmond unopposed. That was the beginning of the invasion of Virginia.

As before, the good came with the bad. In South Carolina General Dan Morgan, who had helped beat Burgoyne in New England, now beat Banastre Tarleton in South Carolina at the Cowpens. Tarleton, with his Legion of light cavalry, was the most daring and dashing of Britain's officers in America; Tarleton was here to-day and gone to-morrow, just ahead of serious trouble, always causing it. This time the two forces were about equal and the fighting lasted less than an hour. At the end, Tarleton managed to escape with his life and a bare handful of men, leaving thirty-nine of his officers dead, two hundred and fifty of his men dead or wounded, and six hundred prisoners. The Americans lost twelve dead and sixty wounded. It was a battle of the same breed as at Kings Mountain. Morgan talked to his men—there were about a thousand on each side—the night before the attack, telling them his plans and what he expected of them. No firing until the enemy was within fifty yards, aim first at the officers. The militia to take the front, fire carefully, then slip back between the ranks of regulars, who were to bear the brunt of the fighting. And in reserve, the cavalry, ready to charge at signal. Next morning he saw that they all had a good hot breakfast. It was open, pine-wood, gently sloping country. They were to use all cover available. Tarleton could not match all that.

Meanwhile a strong military force under General Phillips had been landed from Arnold's ships. Patrick had driven back to Leatherwood, arriving there before Arnold's invasion occurred, but he was worried. He feared that something of the kind was to happen, although Jefferson had not communicated the warnings he'd received. Presently the news of the invasion arrived.

"We're in for it this time, I think," he told Fontaine. "They'll have to call a special session of the Assembly. The Lord be praised, I feel well and can answer at once."

The call came—the Assembly was to meet March 1st, and at Richmond. Arnold had retreated before steadily increasing numbers of American troops to Portsmouth. The members were prompt this time. On the day they met they received the news that La Fayette with a small force of men had reached Virginia, and that Baron von Steuben, too, had crossed the James. Richmond was a mess, of course, but the people were rebuilding and cleaning up. Best of all, the French fleet was due soon with Rochambeau. The Assembly sat three weeks, hard at work. Henry was put at the head of the two most important committees. One quick result was the removal of the inefficient Commissioner of the War Office, and Colonel William Davies, a good and energetic man, took over. Next, two Legions for State service were ordered raised immediately—and were raised, and served to the end of the war, nearer than at the moment seemed likely. And the French fleet would bring an army of its own. Finally, it was decided to issue fifteen million pounds in treasury notes, redeemable at forty to one, and legal tender throughout the State except for contracts payable only in specie.

All these things took up a deal of talk, time, trouble. But in the mass of details handled, Patrick made a graceful motion, unanimously passed. The thanks of the Assembly were to be presented to General Morgan, together with a fine horse, saddled and bridled, and a sword.

The Assembly then adjourned until May 7, 1781. Every one scattered to their homes for the brief period, for Tarleton with a new legion was said to be on his way north, and Tarleton was the expert raider and robber of the British forces. Men wanted to be with their families, in case—

Henry felt that his own place was safe from the marauders, but you could not be sure. He wanted to make careful plans with Colonel Fontaine. The two decided that it would be impossible to save the cattle and horses, but they arranged a safe spot for the valuables owned by the two families, and put bars on two upper rooms to which the women and children could retreat while the pillaging was going on.

Virginia had been sending great reinforcements to

General Greene in the Carolinas, continuing to do so even when Arnold was in Chesapeake Bay, "convincing proof that small expeditions will not frighten that powerful province," as Cornwallis wrote to Clinton, dejectedly. Then, before the Assembly was due to meet in May, the General decided to march for Virginia, join Phillips' army, and crush that "powerful province." He left Wilmington, to which he had been chased by Greene, and reached Petersburg, Virginia, on May 20th. Meantime Phillips had died of the fever and he found Arnold in supreme command. These two British armies, with a detachment recently sent from New York, amounted to more than six thousand five hundred men, some army in those days.

Up in Hanover County La Fayette was waiting to be joined by General Wayne, coming down from the north. Cornwallis decided to get him and his men. "The boy cannot escape me," he announced grandly—but erroneously. With unexpected skill the young commander slipped away bag and baggage to meet Wayne, which he successfully accomplished. Whereupon, deciding that a little robbing would be more fun and certainly more profitable than chasing the Frenchman, Cornwallis made camp on the North Anna.

Meanwhile the Assembly had decided that Richmond was rather too hot a spot in which to meet, with all these Britishers running about within hail, and chose Charlottesville, in Albemarle County, close to Thomas Jefferson's beautiful home, Monticello, standing on the height above the little town. The meeting was delayed by this change, but by May 28th enough of the members had arrived to make it possible to carry on business. Charlottesville had been chosen to accommodate the Governor. He had been there for some time, and now, on the 28th, wrote Washington, "A few days will bring that relief which the constitution has prepared for those oppressed by the duties of my office, and a long-declared resolution of relinquishing it to abler hands has prepared my way to a private station." Nevertheless, he had not resigned and was still Governor of the State, his term ending on June 2nd. Jefferson knew there was bitter feeling against him for his slowness in preparing Virginia against the Arnold invasion, and that there was no chance of reëlection. He preferred, very naturally, to take the initial step himself.

The next act was an adventure that might have been singularly disastrous, and was certainly exciting.

Chapter 18

TARLETON MISSES HIS THROW
AND CORNWALLIS LOSES HIS SWORD

$\mathcal{I}$T was a splendid idea and Tarleton was keen for it. He assured Cornwallis that two hundred and fifty men would be all he required, as there would be no defense. The men lost at the battle of the Cowpens had been replaced; he'd pick the best of them.

"It will give these damned rebels a nasty jolt to lose their entire governing body," Cornwallis declared. "We'll take the whole lot to England in irons. But they must have no warning."

"We'll move fast," Tarleton assured him. He saluted, was gone. Lord, but he was going to enjoy this! He had seventy miles to cover.

It was to take just one man, but the right one, to spoil his game.

Colonel Jack Jouett, whose father kept an inn at Charlottesville, and who had already distinguished himself
under Washington, was spending the night at the Cuckoo
Tavern in Louisa County, on his way home, with dispatches from General Gates for the Assembly. The tavern
was about thirty miles from Charlottesville by the highway.

The night was well along when Jouett was wakened by
the beat of horses' hoofs on the highway. He knew them at
once for cavalry, leaped to the window and saw the long
double row of riders galloping past. No mistaking that
white uniform with green facings, the nodding white
plumes of their hats. Tarleton!

Instantly Jouett realized what the leader was after.
There was no other reason for him to be riding here.

His own blooded mare was in the inn stable. Hurrying
into his clothes, having called a Negro to saddle her, he
was away in fifteen minutes. A hunter, familiar with the
forest trails, he could cut several miles off the distance,
by-pass Tarleton, and reach the town in time to warn
Jefferson and the Assembly. Luckily there was a moon.

At half past four in the morning of June 4th Jefferson,
who liked to rise with the sun, caught sight of a horseman
coming to the house. He stepped out on the portico and
recognized Jack. His mare was caked with mud, Jack's
clothing was torn, his hat gone. The riding through the
narrow forest trails had been rough.

"Good heavens, Colonel, what is it?"

Jouett explained and refusing the Governor's invitation

He leaped to the window and saw a long double
row of riders galloping past.

to dismount and have a swallow of brandy and a bite of food, rode on down the slope to the town, just waking from its sleep.

Instantly the news the rider brought was rushed throughout the little place. The members of the Assembly came hurrying in. Patrick had been up and had his coffee when Jouett arrived at the Swan, the inn his father owned.

"How much time have we, Colonel?" he asked.

"At least an hour, probably more. My mare had been resting twenty-four hours, and she's swifter than the cavalry. I could see the horses were being given a rest at the Court House before I left the highroad."

"Good, we'll have breakfast while our horses are got ready and we can decide where to meet—Staunton, probably. We owe you thanks for this, and so does all Virginia. Destiny rode with you to-night, Colonel Jouett."

Two hours later, when Tarleton came riding in, the birds had flown. Jefferson had sent a message down saying he was taking his family to Poplar Forest, in Bedford County, a farm he owned, a hundred and fifty miles southwest of Charlottesville.

Staunton, fifty miles to the west, was the place selected for the next meeting, to which the Legislature rode in small groups, enough arriving by June 12th to proceed with the business of giving the State a Governor, there having been none since the 2nd. Three men were nominated. General Thomas Nelson, Jr., the perennial John Page, and Thomas Jefferson. Nelson was elected on the first ballot.

Before adjourning on June 23rd George Nicholas, representative from Albemarle County, Jefferson's own, offered this Resolution:

Resolved, that at the next session of the Assembly an inquiry be made into the conduct of the Executive of this State for the last twelve months.

He was seconded by Patrick Henry.

After a great deal of discussion it had been decided, both by the foes and the friends of Jefferson in the Assembly, that such an inquiry was desirable. The bitter criticism current because many all over the State blamed the Governor for the invasion, required an answer. Nicholas asked Henry to second him, which he did, because he thought the question should come into the open, and because he felt that Jefferson had certainly been neglectful.

The inquiry was never held, since before the Assembly met the war was over and the matter had become academic. Jefferson, however, asked Nicholas to send him a copy of the objections on which he had based his Resolution, and defended them in a letter which, while admitting he received the warnings, excused his neglect of them on the ground that although the British expedition was said to be heading southward, it did not definitely designate Virginia, and that it was too expensive and harassing to call out the militia upon an uncertainty. But he could not explain why he had not sent a swift ship to the Capes, to rush back with the news if the fleet were sighted, nor why he had not made everything ready for calling out the militia.

He stood up in the Assembly that met when every one was in state of joy and exultation over war's end and read Nicholas's list of objections with his own answers. Upon which the Assembly passed this Resolution:

Resolved, That the sincere thanks of the General Assembly be given to our former Governor, Thomas Jefferson, Esq., for his impartial, upright, and attentive administration whilst in office. The Assembly wish, in the strongest manner, to declare the high opinion which they entertain of Mr. Jefferson's ability, rectitude and integrity as a chief magistrate of this commonwealth, and mean, by thus publicly avowing their opinion, to obviate and remove all unmerited censure.

It passed without a dissenting voice, although Henry was in his seat. And Jefferson went back to Poplar Forest. That word "unmerited" rankled, however. Later that year, 1781, he worked on his *Notes on the State of Virginia,* and began to vent the hatred he felt for Patrick. Nicholas had visited him and poured out apologies, the two becoming fast friends. Henry made no apologies, not thinking they were called for.

Both Cornwallis and Tarleton devoted the weeks following the Charlottesville fiasco to steady plunder. When they couldn't take all the cattle and sheep on the plantations, they killed them and left them to rot. They sent away thirty thousand slaves all told to the West Indies, and at least ten million dollars' worth of property was stolen or destroyed. They took every horse with them, and cut the throats of colts too young to be useful.

But the people kept their heart up. And in the autumn the light brightened. In August the Count de Grasse from San Domingo sent word he was sailing to Chesapeake Bay with thirty ships of the line and large ground forces. The same month Washington, unknown to Clinton, still entrenched in New York, slipped away for Virginia, receiving at Philadelphia the news that de Grasse was in the great Bay. From Philadelphia, at the head of two thousand Americans and a large number of French, he rode to meet Rochambeau and three thousand French at Williamsburg on September 14th, finding La Fayette there with his own little army. Before this meeting de Grasse had beaten the British fleet outside the Capes, and now the Bay was full of French ships, reaching up into the James and the York, those vessels long blocked at Newport having been freed. Good news, good news from every side! Next came Governor-General Nelson with three thousand Virginia militia, joining Washington's army of twelve thousand. All marched toward Cornwallis, September 28th, scourging him down to Yorktown, while the fleet kept away any attempts at rescue or escape. It was a breathless, amazing advance from every side.

On October 17th Cornwallis ran up the white flag. Two days later he gave up his sword and formally surrendered his entire army, seven thousand men. The war was over. It would take a long while to sign the peace, but the fighting had stopped.

Immediately men on fleet horses spread the glorious news all over the country. There followed processions, cheers, town meetings, resolutions, barbecues, orators, services in the churches. Congress voted thanks to every fighting man, en masse. A Day of Thanksgiving was set aside. And as a final gesture it was voted to set up a great monument at Yorktown. None of those who had fought or voted ever saw it, to be sure, as it wasn't erected until a century had rolled by, but you can see that fine monument to-day.

When, much later, the news reached England Lord North stood for a moment as if paralyzed, then flung up his arms, crying, "My God, so it's all over!" The King still mumbled of conquest to come, but on February 28, 1782, the House of Commons put an end to the long effort to conquer America.

Sixteen years before the surrender Patrick Henry, in the Capitol at Williamsburg, against furious opposition, had carried his Resolutions against the Stamp Act, which proved to be the beginning of the Revolution. He led it, step by step, to the Independence.

"He was," Jefferson told Daniel Webster years after he was dead, "as well-suited to the times as any man ever was, and it is not now easy to say what we should have done without Patrick Henry. He was far before us all in maintaining the spirit of the Revolution... After all it must be allowed that he was our leader in the measures of the Revolution in Virginia, and in that respect more is due to him than to any other man... he left us all far behind."

Considering how often and how wrongly Jefferson criticized Henry these words are worth reading.

Chapter 19

1782 TO 1790—AND GOOD-BY TO POLITICS

RICHMOND had ousted Williamsburg as the capital of Virginia in May, 1779, under Jefferson's governorship. The building of the State Capitol did not begin until 1785 and took seven years to complete. While Jefferson was in France in 1784, negotiating, with John Adams and Benjamin Franklin, treaties of commerce between various European countries and the newly established American Republic, he had sent home the model and plans of the beautiful Maison Carrée at Nîmes as the pattern for Virginia's new Capitol. Appointed Minister to France when Franklin came home in 1785, he stayed abroad till the end of 1789, achieving a great success in the post, and returning to give a careful eye to the finishing of this child of his inspiration. No one who sees it but blesses him as its creator.

Meanwhile the Assembly had to manage as best it could both for its Hall and for the lodging of its members. A charming house was set aside for the Governor, not, of course, comparing with the Palace of the old capitol, but comfortable and dignified. Most of the Legislature boarded with townsfolk or with farmers in the neighborhood until the town gradually recovered from the destruction of war. Sessions were short, almost confined to financial matters, waiting the signature of the Peace Treaty; nothing much to do but rest on your oars till that was completed. The great event occurred on September 3, 1783, and the last British troops left New York on November 25th. In the May session of that year, on the first day of the meeting, Patrick startled the House by introducing and carrying, against considerable opposition, a bill putting an end to the restraint of trade with Great Britain, making the members see his point, in one of his glowing, swinging speeches, that this trade was bitterly needed, and their job was to help recover a vastly needed interchange of goods, instead of keeping it fettered, like a man in chains. With the same sound sense, in the fall session he carried a fight to repeal the Act restraining Tories from returning to their homes and being re-admitted to citizenship. It took all his fire and splendor to win in what came to be called his *Lion and Whelps* speech, which delighted Chancellor Wythe so much that he often used the finale in his classes. Having drawn a clear picture of the usefulness of these past Tories to the State, since they were rich men, enterprising men, Henry finished—"As I have no prejudice in making use of them, so I have no fear of any mischief they can do. Afraid of *them!* What—" he towered, his eyes flashed—"Shall *we,* who have laid the proud British lion at our feet, now be afraid of his whelps?"

So the whelps were permitted to return.

One more contest engaged him before this session ended. A heavy tax bill had been proposed by the rich element of the House led by the Speaker, Judge John Tyler, and won over Henry's objections in the Committee of the Whole. But when it was brought before the whole House Patrick sailed in not only with his arguments that the exhausted people of the back countries must be allowed time to recover, but with a comedy scene that had the whole House shouting with laughter, including Tyler, Page, and Tazewell, who had introduced and backed the tax bill. First he gave a serious sketch of the situation in the upper counties, of the heavy task the people there had to feed their families and keep their homes, then suddenly switched to the ease with which the salt water counties managed:

"What," he demanded, "do the gentlemen who advocate these taxes have to do, except peep and peer along the water running by their estates, pick up a mess of crabs, or paddle off to a rock and rake in the oysters?" And as he spoke Henry peeped and peered, paddled, raked, with the most serious yet hopeful expression, filling an imaginary basket, reaching for more imaginary oysters—until suddenly the laughter swept the House, and he paused, looking at the delighted members with a vague expression of surprise that set them all off again.

When the votes were taken, he won with a majority of more than thirty.

But for some time Henry had been advocating a sensible plan by which Congress would be permitted to lay certain import duties, and so raise money; this measure was passed by the Legislature in June.

At this period he was anxious to have the Federal Government strengthened, and when he agreed to serve in the Assembly in the spring of 1784, he told a small group, including James Madison, that his main reason for doing so was to forward that aim. "Unless something is done to give Congress a compulsory process on delinquent States, I see nothing but inevitable ruin," Henry declared.

It is interesting to get this viewpoint, because later on, when the new Constitution was being ratified by the States, Henry was among those who opposed it, for the reason that it gave what he believed was too powerful a central power.

A high pleasure during this May session for Patrick was the Act passed by the Assembly to order a life-size statue in marble of Washington, to be placed under the dome in the Capitol when the building was ready to receive it. Two busts in marble of La Fayette were also decided upon, one for the Capitol, one for La Fayette himself; but later this was presented to the City of Paris as more appropriate. By Jefferson's excellent advice Jean Antoine Houdon was selected as the sculptor.

Benjamin Harrison's third year as Governor ended in November, 1784, and Henry was again chosen Governor without competition or opposition, and to the very great content of the entire State. Harrison had become Governor at the close of the war when General Nelson had to resign because of illness. He was well liked, but still, so said the people, "There's no man can equal our Henry." His term began on the 30th, but before taking over he rode to Leatherwood to get his family and settle them at a new home, Salisbury, some twelve miles from Richmond. The house was a wide, comfortable frame building, with two pillared porticoes, set in 17,000 acres of field and forest. By now the Henrys had a fine coach and pair, which Dorothea used when she came to Richmond during the sessions of the Legislature to manage the Governor's house, give parties, and, as Judge Spencer Roane tells us, live "as genteely and associate with as polished society as any Governor before or since has done, entertaining as much company as others and in as genteel a style."

Before this year ended two deaths, his mother's and his brother William's, came to grieve him. A little later his last surviving aunt followed them.

The two years, 1785-86, during which Henry was Governor of his State on this second stretch were filled with a lot of troublesome affairs. The Indian troubles broke out again, Kentucky began to agitate for separate statehood, and a certain Colonel Arthur Campbell got up a petition to Congress to have Virginia separated into two states by the Alleghanies, largely because of great irritation in that western part of the State over the militia laws. Henry got the militia trouble settled, checked the Colonel, and a little later the Assembly passed an Act making the setting up of an independent government within the bounds of Virginia, except by due action of the Assembly, high treason. At the same time it agreed to Kentucky's demand, "so soon as a convention of her people desired it, and Congress gave its consent."

One matter that had long troubled Patrick was the severity of the law, brought from England, which imposed the death sentence for many sorts of crimes, often mere robberies without violence. During the Legislature's second meeting, in 1785, he got an Act passed authorizing conditional pardons, except for murder or treason, followed the next year by the start of a careful penitentiary system. Nor did he merely see that an act was passed. He took the time to write to Charles Pearson, Sergeant of Richmond, these humane directions as to the care of the city's prisoners:

Particular care must be taken that they have plenty of wholesome food and that their clothes are warm and comfortable. Two duffell blankets must be had for each man. . . . You are to take care that their clothes and lodging be kept clean, and that their labor is confined to the usual hours and good weather. In case of sickness you are to apply to Dr. Foushee.

From the state of confinement in which these people have remained lately it is necessary for you to be careful that they avoid such a degree of exposure and labor as may be safely practiced by persons who have not been confined. Their progress to a full share of labor must be gradual. You are also to see that they be not restrained from divine worship, and attend them accordingly.

No such directions had ever been issued a Sergeant of Police in this world until Patrick Henry wrote them. They might be studied with advantage to-day in all too many of our prisons. Henry had also been the moving cause in having the Act authorizing the manumission of slaves passed in 1782; it seemed to him there was no fitter way of celebrating the liberty achieved for themselves, than in making it lawful for any slave holder to free his Negroes, should he so desire.

In April, 1786, Colonel William Christian was killed fighting the Indians, and buried on the estate he had acquired in Kentucky, Oxmoor, near Louisville. This was heartbreaking. Henry loved his sister Anne above his other sisters, and Will and he had long been devoted friends. He wrote, "Would to God I could say something to give relief to the dearest of women and sisters... I forbear to tell you how great was my love for my friend and brother." And he was glad that she had a son-in-law who could take charge of her affairs, and told her, "While I am endeavoring to comfort you I need a comforter myself."

But the autumn brought him the happiness of seeing his two younger daughters by his first marriage married to fine men, Anne in September to Spencer Roane, later Judge Roane, and Elizabeth to Philip Aylette in October.

A serious dispute racked the entire country during the latter part of Henry's second year as Governor. It was started when Spain demanded that she be left sole mistress of the Mississippi Valley, and of all navigation on the Father of Waters as far as the Ohio. Spain's envoy was Don Diego Guardoqui and he hied him straight to the Northern states where he presented letters to John Jay, the New York statesman, who had visited Spain during the war to negotiate a loan and guarantee that country the possession of Florida; Spain had not been responsive, though a small loan was obtained, together with a strong hint that the Mississippi claims put forward by America must be waived.

The Northern and Eastern states were offered open ports in Spain, the purchase from them of all the timber necessary to build the new Spanish Navy planned for immediate construction, and other inducements pleasing to a country that was hard up. As for the Mississippi, these states didn't give a whoop for it. Seven agreed to sign the wished-for treaty, and started a strong attempt to push it through in Congress, nearly succeeding, although the Articles of Confederacy made nine the number necessary for a winning vote. But the Mississippi and its eastern valley meant everything to the South, pushing steadily westward and using the great Father of Waters as a valuable trading road.

At long last this attempt to better the Northern states by sacrificing the Southern ones was beaten. Henry, backed by his Legislature, threw all his strength against it; but it had an unexpected effect. For Henry, until then an advocate of powerful Federal centralization, suddenly saw that tyranny might lie that way.

His second term as Governor ended with the last day of November, 1786. A month before, he wrote sister Anne: "I shall resign my office next month and retire, my wife and myself being heartily tired of the bustle we live in here." He had already bought a plantation with a comfortable house on the Appomattox in Prince Edward County, near the excellent college of Hampden-Sydney, where the two young sons of his first marriage could finish their education, and in early spring, 1787, the family moved there.

Salisbury and some other land had been sold to pay for the new home, but the salary of the Governor was nowhere near equal to the "genteel" demands upon it. Henry was in debt, and said as much to Colonel Holcomb, a friend of several years standing, from whom he'd bought the new place.

"I'm troubled, Holcomb. I'm fifty years old, the governorship has cost me a deal more than I received. I'm badly in debt, and I don't like it."

"If you want my advice, Patrick, get back to the law. Your tongue will soon pay your debts. If you'll promise me you will, I'll give you a retaining fee on the spot."

"I think you're right, and I'll promise—I'd like to get back into the law, for that matter."

"Well, here's your fee," returned Holcomb, handing

over five pounds. It was the first Patrick had received since 1774, and he took it, smiling.

But a new step was being taken by the country. A Constitution was to be written. Delegates had been chosen by twelve states, Rhode Island refusing to join, on May 25, 1787.

Here was matter to engage all Henry's energy for the present. He was elected as one of the seven Virginia delegates to the Constitutional Convention. He refused it, although Edmund Randolph, who had been elected Governor of the State, wrote him begging him to come. He gave no reason other than "it is with much concern that I feel myself constrained to decline acting under this appointment." Madison was greatly distressed by this refusal, as was the Governor; it was generally conceded that the Mississippi affair was at the bottom of it. The fact was that Henry wished to stay free to comment on the results of the Convention, free to fight them if he thought best. The meeting was to be held in Philadelphia. In October Henry was elected to the Virginia Legislature as a member from Prince Edward County.

Behind closed doors, for four months, the delegates worked in Philadelphia, finishing the tremendous job September 17th. Immediately after returning to Mount Vernon Washington sent copies of the document to several leading men, Patrick of course among them. He had been president of the convention, and he wrote Henry: "I wish the constitution which is offered had been more perfect; but I sincerely believe it is the best that could be obtained at this time. And, as a constitutional door is opened for amendments hereafter, the adoption of it, under the present circumstances of the Union is in my opinion desirable ... the convention has been looked up to, by the reflecting part of the community, with a solicitude that is hardly to be conceived; and if nothing had been agreed on by that body, anarchy would soon have ensued..."

Henry returned a letter expressing his sincere and heartfelt thanks and his appreciation of what fatigue and toil must have been suffered by the delegates, at the same time lamenting that, "I cannot bring my mind to accord with the proposed Constitution. The concern I feel is really greater than I can express..."

He was by no means alone in his feeling. On his side was George Mason, that deep student and fine mind, Richard Henry Lee, the Cabells, General Thomas Nelson and his relative, W. Nelson, St. George Tucker, John Taylor, the Judges of the State Supreme Court, Monroe, Tyler, Benjamin Harrison. Henry was their leader, as George Washington was the first of the Federalists, who numbered among them John Marshall, later the greatest Chief Justice of the United States Supreme Court the country has ever known, Pendleton, Wythe, and James Madison. Washington did not attend the meetings, which began on June 2, 1778, but his influence remained tremendous. It was Madison who led against Henry. Madison was a cool, temperate, thoughtful speaker, his reasoning sound and clearly given. He had followed every step of the building of the Constitution, and like Washington believed it good. Henry feared that Congress, controlling the militia and with its power to tax the country's wealth—"the sword in one hand and the purse in the other," as Henry worded it —possessed all the power while the people had no legal defence against this power. He warned that the Constitution "as it stands, has an awful squinting; it squints toward monarchy...your President may easily become your king."

For twenty-three days the battle raged. Richmond was crowded, and the larger Hall into which the Assembly had moved, packed to bursting. By June 23rd the Federalists felt fairly certain of success, if they ceded in the matter of amendments. Wythe moved for ratification. Henry countered with a proposal that the amendments and a Bill of Rights should first be passed. That plunged them into the whirlpool again for two more days. Dramatically, when Henry was making his final speech and as, lifting his arms in a wide gesture, he called on the powers above to interfere, to reveal the fatal imperfections of the plan offered, a furious thunderstorm burst over them, rolling and flashing, while the wind fairly shook the building. And there stood Henry, seeming to make the storm his ally, his voice chiming with the thunder, his eyes flashing with the lightning, his face now hidden, now revealed as the storm blazed or blackened.

The storm rolled off, Henry sat down. The voting on the two resolutions began. Wythe's carried, 89 to 79, Henry's lost, 80 to 88. The long fight was over.

Next morning both sides closed with gentle words. Madison said, "Let us join with cordiality in those alterations we think proper." And Henry, "Whether I win or lose I shall remain a peaceable citizen, my head, my heart, my hand at liberty to retrieve the loss of liberty, working to remove the defects of the system in a constitutional way."

That same evening, when the losers met to talk things over and decide what to do, Henry proved he meant what he said. A number among them proposed resistance to the new government. He refused. "I did my duty in opposing the Constitution in the proper place and with all the power I have. As true and faithful republicans, let us go home ... let us give the government fair aid and support."

Henry had fought for twenty amendments and a bill of rights. Much of the rest of 1778 was occupied in districting the State, which Henry did not take part in, going home where a lot of law business had piled up for him, beginning as soon as he announced his return to the bar. When the election of the State's two Senators and their Representatives took place Henry worked to get anti-Federalists into office, since Congress must vote on the amendments to the Constitution. He nominated Richard Henry Lee and William Grayson, and won, even over Madison, who had been backed by Washington.

Washington, of course, received a unanimous vote as President, and no man was gladder than Patrick, though George had cooled off toward him because of his opposition to the Constitution. This coolness vanished in time and the friendship between the two men was restored. The inauguration, taking place in New York City, March 4, 1789, passed off magnificently, and the new government took office. Since the old Confederation Congress had fizzled out during the past October the country had been for four months without a National Government.

After a hard fight in the new Congress the first ten of Henry's twenty amendments were adopted, and a year later the eleventh. It is easy to see their importance when you read them, yet they passed only by the threat, backed by Patrick Henry and Governor Clinton of New York, also an anti-Federalist, of calling another Convention, to which the Federalists were desperately opposed.

Chapter 20

THE LAST MILES

*W*HEN Patrick Henry returned to his home, to private life and to the law, he was, certainly by modern criteria, still a fairly young man, at least a man who should be in his prime. At the end of May, 1790, he would be fifty-four. But the poison of malaria was in his blood, and there was no way, then, of combating that poison. You had your ups and downs. Cold weather and change of climate were the only suggestions doctors had to give, each a palliative, neither a cure. Henry looked ten years older than he was, his stoop was much exaggerated at times; yet in keenness of mind, as also in human interest, he was young as ever. He liked people, he loved his family, his children were an endless delight to him—and almost an endless chain. He was as hospitable a man as any in that hospitable state of his, a witty host, and amusing in his own family. Also a deeply religious man without being anchored to any creed, or opposed to any whose fountainhead was the Bible and the teachings of Christ. That fountainhead was water of life to him, and never a day passed that did not have a space of time devoted to it. When he was at home he used, always an early riser, to sit in the dining room in one of the windows, reading from his Bible until the family had collected, and breakfast was served.

The latest-to-arrive baby had been born during Patrick's fight against the Constitution. In the middle of a speech he had seen one of his elder sons in the Hall, and as soon as he reached a place where he could pause, he left the platform and hurried toward the lad.

"Your mother?" Dorothea had always been "mother" to his first family from the time she became Patrick's wife.

"She's feeling splendidly, Father, and it's a boy."

"Alexander Spottswood—your mother and I agreed on that name before I left." He hurried back to his speech.

Father and son supped together that evening, the one as happy as the other, and when young Charles rode home next morning he carried with him a gift for Dorothea.

It was not long before Henry had more demands for his services as a lawyer than he could handle. He charged the highest fees in the State, high even, considering the difference in the value of money, for this day. Also, he insisted that his clients must always engage associate counsel to prepare the cases for him ready for trial. Some people who didn't like him growled that all he cared about was money; they forgot he had given years of his life to his country with little or no pay, and that he had a very large family to care for. Remembering his own father's last days Patrick was determined to leave both his sons and daughters, let alone his wife, safely provided for. Like Washington, he was an excellent man of business, and some training he had had as a surveyor gave him a knowledge of land. He bought and sold a deal of it, almost always at a fair profit. No, he did not mean to spend his last years poor and dependent, if good sense, hard work, and his great talent as an advocate could prevent it. He knew he could not have many more years to live. He had given his strength and his time to his country. Now he meant to lay by, not for himself, but his family.

A great many of his cases were in defense of alleged criminals, and with these his success was phenomenal. It must be remembered that Henry would not take cases without a personal conviction either of his client's innocence, or of mitigating circumstances strongly in his favor. Then he cared not at all how dark the matter looked. There are endless yarns told about him, some trifling, like the one of a pair of young lovers. They were much in love, but the girl was under age, and her parents refused their consent to a marriage. According to the law, if the man ran away with her he could be sentenced to prison. He came to Henry. Was there anything to be done?

Patrick took care to assure himself that the would-be groom was of good character and able to support a wife. He asked for a private interview with the girl:

"You truly love this young man? And are assured of his love?"

"Indeed, Sir, we truly love each other. Father wants me to marry a man of his own choosing, but..."

Henry nodded—he understood the buts of life.

"Very well. Listen, this is what I want you to do. Make a

rendezvous with your sweetheart, and ride there to meet him on one of your father's horses. Tell him he is to mount behind you, ride to the nearest preacher, get married. He'll be arrested, but I'll see him through."

The marriage took place; so did the arrest. At the trial, before a crowded courtroom, the commonwealth's attorney, stating the plain facts, left the law to act. Then Henry got to his feet:

"I admit the law is precisely as has been stated, Sir. But I want to ask the young lady a few questions. Will she please take the stand."

Somewhat shyly, the girl did so:

"Please tell the Court just what occurred."

"I rode one of father's horses to the spot where I had asked Harry to meet me. Then I begged him to climb up behind me, and ran away with him to the preacher's."

"Did he run away with you?"

"No, Sir, it was I who ran away with him."

"Oh, I see," said Henry slowly. "*You* ran away with him!" He beamed at the Court, receiving a broad grin from his Honor. The crowd roared with laughter and the young man was set free, the newly married pair being given a great reception when they followed the crowd outside.

Another very different case was tried in the New London Court House. A certain John Hook, Scot and one-time Tory, had a store in the town carrying provisions and live stock. He brought suit against John Venable, formerly a commissary of the Continental Army. At the time when Cornwallis was invading Virginia and there was difficulty in finding food, Mr. Venable had seized two of Hook's steers. He had not observed all the legalities in so doing, and now Hook was bringing action for trespass and claiming damages. Henry wasted no time trying to disprove the illegality of the seizure. But he drew a striking picture of the cold, hungry soldiers, of what a little meat meant to them. It was grim; the audience stirred, growled. "Where," demanded Henry, "is the man who had an American heart in his bosom who would not throw his home, his barns, his fields open to those famished patriots? Where? There he stands—but whether the heart of an American beats in his bosom, you, gentlemen, are to judge."

Then he swung abruptly to the American triumph at Yorktown, with the shouts of victory, the cry of "Washington and Liberty!", the joy in every voice echoing back from hills and river: "But hark! What note of discord disturbs the general joy and silences the acclamations of victory?" He paused, his head bent, listening, then, "It is the note of *John Hook*, hoarsely bawling through the American camp, 'Beef! Beef! Beef!' "

The jury brought back a verdict for Mr. Hook of one penny and one penny costs, to be paid by Mr. Venable.

From one court to another Henry drove in his little gig drawn by a fine horse, his favorite slave, Jack White, who was half Indian, going with him on all his longer jaunts to drive and take care of the animal. He went far beyond his own county, and always found a large audience waiting for him. "Henry's going to be on the case," was enough to pack any courthouse. One of his fascinations was the power he had to swing from the sublime to the ridiculous, as in the case against a friend of his, Richard Randolph, for the murder of an infant, claimed by the mother to be Randolph's illegitimate child. Naturally a vast deal of excitement attended the case, and Randolph had not been allowed bail. He was, however, innocent, as was absolutely proved several years later when the actual father confessed. Henry never doubted his innocence, but a lot of bad feeling had been stirred up against the man, who belonged to one of the great families and was wealthy.

Randolph was defended by Alexander Campbell, a famous advocate, John Marshall, appointed Chief Justice of the United States Supreme Court a few years later, and Patrick Henry. Henry's part was to examine the witnesses.

Now, a lady, daughter of Archibald Cary, (the same man who'd sworn he'd kill "Dictator" Henry years ago) who had married and come to the vicinity, was the most important witness against the defendant. Patrick saw at once that she was furious at being examined, and asked her teasingly a number of seemingly idle questions; yet her answers built up a certain feeling against her as being prejudiced and what we might call nosey. She asserted that she had become suspicious, and under Henry's urging admitted that on one occasion, when staying in the Randolph house with the plaintiff, she had been given the room next to her. There was a crack in the door between the two rooms and "I tried to satisfy my curiosity by peeping through it."

Henry led her on. Just what had she seen? Nothing absolutely—it was difficult to get much of a view. But she was sure the lady wasn't alone. Where was the crack? Rather low down. Did she have to lean down, or would she show the Court how she managed? So she knelt down, with a furious glance over her shoulder. Patrick kept on, drawing her to admit her inability to get any real view, although she did manage to see that the lady was undressing.

All the while Henry's voice held a note of faint ridicule, while the witness grew angrier and began to be very flustered. Suddenly he leaned toward her and in a voice of deep seriousness asked:

"And which eye did you peep with?"

The court room audience could not hold in any longer

and burst into laughter. The witness suddenly realized she
was being made fun of, had been trapped into proving
herself a gossip and a scandalmonger. As for Henry, he
turned to the Court and, speaking from the heart, he cried,
"Great God, deliver us from eavesdroppers!"

As to the witness, she was completely discredited with
the jury.

Mr. Randolph was acquitted but the accusation broke
his heart. He was a sensitive, gentle spirit and the very
thought that he could have been so accused was too much
for him. He died within three or four years, before the
truth came out, which seems a pity.

Such scenes and incidents were countless, and before
Henry ceased to practice, in 1794, no two practicing lawyers could meet together without chuckling over some
personal experience with him, or some story told them.
John Marshall, who often appeared on the same cases with
him, admitted that Henry was a powerful orator, but, he
added, "He was much more than that. He was a learned
lawyer, a most accurate thinker and a profound reasoner."

One more of Henry's triumphs must be included, the
great British Debt Cause. Like the Parsons' Cause of years
earlier, this case took more than one year to settle. Henry,
Marshall, James Innes, and Alexander Campbell—he, by
the way, was a cousin of the poet, Thomas Campbell—were
engaged by the defendants. And the pleadings began when
the United States Court opened at Richmond in 1790 with
many British creditors suing to recover money that had
already been paid by the creditors to the State.

The crux of the matter was that by the treaty with
Britain America had agreed that British debts could be
recovered in America. But as far back as 1777 Virginia,

acting as a sovereign State, had ordered all such debts paid into her own Treasury, and two years later the Legislature had passed an Act of Forfeiture, vesting all British property in the Commonwealth. These acts were passed before there was a United States or a treaty. Now these persons were being asked to pay the debts all over again. A bit thick!

Henry had to qualify for the Federal Circuit Court. This he did on November 23, 1791, and a few months later the same day the first of the British Debt cases was called. It was to be a test. It was also a test for Henry, and he had prepared for it by days of intense study, not seeing his family, having his meals served in his office on a tray, reading, reading, reading from Vattel's *Law of Nations,* making notes and heads of arguments in a small volume an inch thick, which he could stuff into his pocket. By the time he reached Richmond he knew every principle of law, national and municipal, touching the subject. He was completely ready and at ease.

Men who had heard him often before were astonished anew at Patrick's eloquence, and when in the spring of 1793 the end was reached and he raised his hands "in one of his grand, solemn pauses," there was a general suppressed applause and the Associate Judge cried out, loudly enough for those nearest to hear, "Gracious God! He is an orator indeed!"

This Associate Justice was James Iredell. He had never heard Henry speak, and had himself been quite outspoken in his belief that he was certainly greatly overrated by his admirers, though willing to admit he must be unusual; he had written his wife just before Henry was due to speak, "We began on the British causes the second day of the court, and are now in the midst of them. The great Patrick Henry is to speak to-day." Patrick spoke and Iredell became one of these admirers, nor ever hesitated to say so.

Henry's argument, amply backed by citations from the law of nations and decisions of famous justices, was that contracts between countries that had gone to war with each other were void. War was a struggle so great, a struggle to the death, that it killed not only things involving pounds and pence, but other, far more human and far greater things. He also cited the fact that Britain had already broken the treaty in several instances. He reminded his listeners that the enemy had brutally plundered the country. Why, then, should these debts be considered sacred?

The really amazing thing about the whole matter is that Henry spoke on it for three consecutive days. It turned entirely on law. Yet Henry brought to it so great a human quality that each day the room was packed, each day he was listened to in a deep yet responsive silence by a mixed audience, most with no personal interest whatever in the question being discussed. And at the end, when he sat down, there was a prolonged murmur of appreciation, a stirring, as though the audience had been present at the acting of a great human drama, as indeed they had.

The Court's decision agreed with Henry's interpretation. The defendants were allowed credit for the sum they had payed into the State Treasury. Henry had triumphed in the Circuit Court of the United States. But when, after Henry had left the bar, the case was appealed to the Supreme Court, it reversed the findings of the Circuit Court, on the ground that the treaty, being the supreme law under the Constitution, annulled the Acts of Virginia, although she was sovereign when they were passed.

George Mason was not present at Henry's final pleading. He had died in October of 1792, as so many men in those past years did die, of malarial poisoning, from which he had long suffered. His going was a bitter sorrow to his friend. The two men had grown ever closer, especially during the excursions and alarums of the fight against the Constitution.

Chapter 21

QUIET HAVEN

THROUGH the year 1794 Patrick cleared up all his law cases, and resigned. At the end of that year Robert Brook, Governor of the State, tried in vain to persuade him to take a lawsuit of great importance for the Commonwealth; and earlier in the year he had declined to accept nomination as Senator of the United States. He was tired out, and sensing that he probably had not many more years to live, he wanted to live them at home, with the family and friends he loved. Already death had taken its toll. In 1791 his first grandson, Edmund Fontaine, just starting in the law, passed away suddenly, followed a few months later by his father. Late in the same winter Patrick's widowed sister Anne, who had come from Kentucky with tuberculosis and by doctor's advice gone to the West Indies, finding herself growing worse rather than better, took ship for home—only to be buried at sea. Then, in this year of Henry's retirement, he lost his Neddie, youngest son of his first marriage, as well as his longtime friend, Richard Henry Lee, only four years older than himself. And George Mason, too, was dead.

The plantation to which Henry now came was not the Prince Edward home. In 1792 when his two sons had graduated from Hampden-Sydney College, and Henry himself was recovered from the serious illness he suffered that year, Dorothea and he decided to get back to the higher country. They drove together to see an estate offered them in Campbell County, named after Henry's Tory-hating brother-in-law, which was but fifty miles northeast of Leatherwood, in the same bold, colorful country with peaks and rolling forested hills, rushing streams, and plenty of game. Indians still lived in the district, and so did bears, plenty of them. Dolly and Patrick liked the place at once.

The house with its gardens was on an island in the clear Staunton River just below where it had been joined by the swift Otter, coming tumbling from the mountains. Long Island was its name. With it Henry bought thirty-five hundred acres of excellent land. Next, two years later, there was a second purchase, eighteen miles further down the Staunton, over the border into Charlotte County. This place was known as Red Hill, because of the red bluffs rising above a bend in the river that half-circled the plateau on which the house stood. He and Dorothea added this new home to the other so that the children would not be too remote from social affairs. The girls were reaching into their teens, and within easy riding from Red Hill there were a number of families in other charming houses, with young people of their own. Patrick and Dorothea were also pleased to have friends near, both being hospitable folk. At first most of the year was spent at Long Island, then only half the year, and finally, in 1796, Red Hill had won them completely. Long Island was given to the care of an agent, and Patrick contented himself with an occasional visit to see how everything was getting along.

Virginian hospitality is famous, and certainly the Henrys were worthy of the tradition. Breakfast was an early affair, but that didn't prevent visitors from dropping in most mornings, and finding room at the big table amid the laughter and chatter of the family. Dinner was usually served at half past twelve, and often there were as many as twenty invited guests to that meal. In addition Dorothea made a custom of having a long table in the wide hall set out with cold snacks, sandwiches and sweets, so that a caller at whatever hour could have a tasty bite.

Red House faced south, with a glorious view of Staunton Valley, a view Henry loved. Here, under a tree, on the lawn, and close to one of the eight springs, all having a slight content of lithia, all busy digging their small ravines down the slope at the top of which the house stood, he used to spend some hours of the afternoon in the fine days of spring, summer, and autumn, comfortably seated with a table beside him. Books and his correspondence, which was considerable, occupied those hours, which were kept sacred from any interference. Always there was a gourd full of spring water beside him. As the hour for supper drew near Dorothea usually joined him, and the two would sit chatting, enjoying the view and each other until a servant summoned them to table.

After supper Patrick liked to play with the younger

children, talking with them, listening to them, treating them as friends and equals, as was always his way. And then, in the gentle hour or two following the setting of the sun, with the mockingbirds singing, out might come violin or flute. The various members of the family would come and go, bringing the gossip of the day, planning this or that excursion or visit, and presently it was bedtime. Hours were early. The one that came with the rising sun always found Patrick up and out, in spring through fall, if it were clear. The best hour of the day, he insisted, was this one, crystal clear, cool, windless. He liked to walk to a hillcrest overlooking his wide, undulating fields, and the long slopes down from the ridge, the westward one given up to pastures and dotted with cattle and sheep, the eastward planted to tobacco. Far down in the fields the Negroes were beginning work, and in that still hour their master would call out directions and orders for the day. His voice, melodious as an Alpine horn, would carry half a mile or more, his enunciation perfectly distinct. There was no trouble understanding him.

Although the malarial attacks gave Henry no more trouble, he was aging swiftly. They had sapped his vitality, and in 1796 he looked to be seventy rather than sixty. This fact, as well as his yearning to be undisturbed in his home, made him refuse two important posts in 1794, one a nomination to be Secretary of State in Washington's Cabinet, the second to be a Judge in the United States Supreme Court. The misunderstanding between Washington and Henry caused by false reports of savage criticisms by Washington of Henry in regard to his attitude toward the Constitution, naming him a "factious, seditious character," had been ended when Governor Henry Lee wrote the President of these reports and of how sorely they had hurt Henry. The President instantly answered, denying anything of the kind had ever so much as entered his mind, and that though the two had differed on the question of the Constitution, "I have always respected and esteemed him," and moreover had never ceased to be grateful for what Henry had done in regard to the anonymous letter at the time of the secret attempt to oust Washington from the command of the American Army. Governor Lee sent the letter to Henry and the shadow between the two men disappeared.

Two children, a boy and a girl, were born to the Henrys at Red Hill, and their two elder daughters were married from the house. It was a lovely house in the prevailing mode, long, deep, a story-and-a-half high. A beautiful, pillared portico reached by circular steps accented the front, flanked in the usual manner by two tall windows on each side. Years later his son, John Henry, who inherited it, put an upper story on one side of the building, spoiling somewhat the general harmony of line. On either side gardens hedged with box were sweet with flowers, and behind the house Henry had a small building he used as his office. The room had no ceiling, only the sharply ridged roof. "I like to hear the rain falling on the shingles," Patrick told his wife.

In the winter mornings Henry kept up his habit of going early to the breakfastroom and reading the Bible while the family gathered. As each one entered he would greet him or her with "Goodmorrow," and when all were seated, including his wife, he closed the Book and took his own place.

In 1798 a bitter dispute arose between the two parties of the government, the Republican and the Democratic,

concerning the right of a State either to secede from the
Union in case it disapproved of the interpretation of some
item of the Constitution by the Government, or to nullify
the interpretation. The States were to decide according to
their own convictions, the claim being that the Constitution was only a compact between Sovereign States. Jefferson was on that side, opposing Washington and Henry.
When Virginia approved the Constitution, it created, in
Henry's opinion, the Nation of the people of the United
States. He did not like the extent of the powers granted,
but he did believe that such a union was essential to the
country. Now the Kentucky and Virginia Resolutions upholding the States' rights to annul or secede had been
passed, and in January, 1799, Washington wrote to Henry
appealing to him to be a candidate, "if not for Congress,
which you may think would take you too long from home
(for Henry had recently been obliged to refuse Washington's desire to send him to France as a Special Envoy to
settle, with a distinguished group, the difficulties that had
sprung up since France's Revolution between the two
countries), then as a candidate for representative in the
General Assembly... I conceive it to be of immense importance at this crisis that you should be there..."

For some weeks Henry had been ill, part of the time tied
to his bed, but he did not hesitate. He at once declared
himself a candidate for the House of Delegates at the
approaching election, and gave notice that he would speak
to the people of Charlotte on county court day, the first
Monday in March.

Most of the people in Charlotte County had never seen,
far less heard Patrick Henry. On the appointed day all of
them who could make it were there, waiting.

He had driven to the meetingplace with his wife and a

few old friends, the group finding chairs ready for them on the porch of the tavern facing the square. Slowly the crowd increased, pouring in from all parts of the county and from next-by Campbell County until there were thousands crowded around the porch and into the square. When the time to speak came Henry got to his feet with some difficulty, for he was still weak from his illness. He looked haggard, and began hesitatingly, his voice barely heard. Then, as of old, he straightened and lifted, his eyes grew brilliant, he looked young and ardent, and his voice rang clear and melodious, so that even the outer row of listeners had no trouble hearing him.

He told of his anxiety, his alarm to find Virginia ready to leave the sphere into which she had been placed by the Constitution, to which she had agreed freely, as a free Commonwealth. Also, that she had ventured to pronounce on the validity of Federal laws, outside her jurisdiction. Such opposition by Virginia to the Acts of the General Government could have but one end; enforcement by military power. And to what could that lead but civil war? What, he wanted to know, would Virginia think, and how would she act, if the county of Charlotte disputed the laws of Virginia, refused to obey them? If the people thought the alien and sedition laws passed by Congress were wrong, they held the reins over Congress, and by petition could bring the subject to a head. "The Congress are as much our representatives as the Assembly, and have as good a right to our confidence."

He begged his hearers to think well before they started action to "split into factions that union on which our existence as a nation hangs." He warned that they were risking the existence of representative government, and that, once lost, it could never be retrieved. "Let us not exhaust ourselves in civil commotions and internecine wars."

He ended with this statement:

"I mean to do all that is in my power to allay these heart-burnings and jealousies that have been stirred up; and if I am unable to do it I hope another man will take up the task."

As Henry spoke Dorothea and the friends with her exchanged relieved, triumphant looks. They had feared that his strength could not answer the demands he would put on it, that the power and the fire for which he was famous would not come at his call. They need not have been troubled. There was about him, said many who heard him that day, a majesty, a harmony of voice, of expression, an effect both of gentleness and strength, that held his audience breathless as if under a spell. They had come to hear a famous speaker, and they had heard a great man.

This was the last speech, the last public appearance of Patrick Henry. He returned home exhausted and went to bed, but was uneasy lying down and spent most of his time in a great armchair. In April he was elected to the Legislature. Jefferson, true to form, and furious that Henry had returned to public life, wrote Archibald Stuart—"The state elections have generally gone well. Mr. Henry will have the mortification of encountering such a mass of talent as he has never met before, for from everything I can hear we never had an abler nor a sounder legislature. His apostasy must be unaccountable to those who do not know all the recesses of his heart."

Did he imagine he knew Henry's heart? And apostasy? There was none. From the first Henry had considered, and openly upheld this opinion, that once the Constitution was adopted by the States it made of them one nation, their individual sovereignty merged into one whole. They could pass amendments, and they were left the right of revolution. And to this he clung, and to this he spoke.

As it happened, Henry was not to meet the "sound and able Legislature" Jefferson declared would be too much for him. He had another rendezvous.

By May there was no doubt but that Patrick was seriously ill. Fortunately a great friend of Henry's, one who had seen him through several illnesses, Dr. George Cabell, of Lynchburg, forty miles away, was able to come, and to stay with the sick man.

It was not the old enemy, malaria, but an intestinal trouble, already far advanced. For months Dorothea had been greatly troubled because of her husband's loss of appetite and consequent loss of weight. He had always been a light eater, he had always been thin, but even at his political meeting in March, those friends who had not seen him for some time were shocked at the haggardness of his face, at his bodily weakness. Then, back in the home he loved, he seemed to recover; his interest in the campaign going on all over Virginia was keen, his plans for the coming sojourn in Richmond when the Legislature should meet went forward. Dorothea was to go with him.

Then, suddenly, he was worse. When Dr. Cabell arrived, toward the middle of May, he was alarmed. Henry was steadily growing weaker. At the end of the month he wrote to his daughter, Martha Fontaine, at Leatherwood, "Dear Patsy [this was her father's pet name for her], I am very unwell, and Dr. Cabell is with me." She lost no time, arriving with her remaining son, Patrick Henry Fontaine. Other relatives scattered here and there were notified, and began to gather. But his daughters, Anne, the wife of Spencer Roane, and Elizabeth Aylett, could not come. Anne was visiting her sister and was ill. On June 1st a letter arrived addressed to Patrick. Anne had suddenly died. The letter was not given to him; they dared not give it, for fear the news would kill him.

Seated in the great chair, for he could no longer bear lying down, Patrick waited. He had his Bible within reach, and laying it down one morning, when grandson Patrick came to sit with him, he said thoughtfully, "I should be wretched at this moment, my boy, if I had not made my peace with God." He felt the grief of leaving the wife, the numerous family he loved so dearly, but he accepted approaching death with tranquillity. He had no fear of it, nor complaint. He had lived his life fully, honestly. Time now to go.

Dr. Cabell had been able to do nothing except ease the pain. On the morning of June 6th he sat beside Henry, quiet in his chair. Another crisis of pain was coming. The doctor handed his patient a small phial containing a dose of liquid mercury.

Patrick looked at it, then raised his eyes to his friend:

"I suppose, Doctor, this is your last resort?"

Cabell nodded, his own eyes grave.

"I'm sorry—it is. Acute inflammation of the intestines has already occurred; unless it is stopped, mortificaton must follow, if it has not already done so—I fear ..."

"What will be the effect of this medicine?"

"It will give you immediate relief—" he stopped.

"Or, Doctor, it may prove fatal—immediately?" and Henry gave him one of his faint smiles.

"In any case, you can only live a very short time. This may relieve you."

"Then excuse me for a few moments, Doctor." He drew

down over his eyes the silken cap he wore, and in a clear voice, very simply, he said a prayer for his family, for his country, and for his own soul. Then, calm as ever, swallowed the medicine, and leaned back quietly.

Dr. Cabell loved him. Unable to keep back his grief, he left the room and rushed outside, where he threw himself down under a tree, shaken with sobs, his head buried in his arms. When he was able to recover himself he went back. Henry was surrounded by his family, all pain gone. Dorothea, who had entered the room as the Doctor came out, knelt close to him, one of his arms resting on her shoulder. Patrick was speaking, little words of affection, of leavetaking. He looked at Cabell as he entered, and the doctor leaned over him, his fingers on his pulse. The two had often held long arguments about religion, for Cabell was not a believer.

"Doctor," Patrick said, very slowly, very softly, "you see how great a thing it is to a man when the time to die comes, to have faith in the reality and beauty of religion—" he drew a barely perceptible breath, another...

"After which," we are told, by one of those present, "they who were looking at him saw that his life had departed."

The garden walk at Red Hill leads onward to a space some fifty feet square, hedged by tall box. In the center are two marble slabs side by side, resting, slightly raised above the ground, on a supporting base of matched stones. As you stand at the foot of this single tomb the slab to the right is inscribed:

TO THE MEMORY OF PATRICK HENRY
Born May 29, 1736. Died June 6, 1799
His Fame his best Epitaph

The one to the left:

TO THE MEMORY OF
DOROTHEA DANDRIDGE
Wife of Patrick Henry
Born 1755. Died February 14, 1831

Lifting your eyes, you see, above the hedge, and backed by trees, the sloping roof and gable of Red Hill.

(1)

This book is made in full compliance with Government Directive L 120 limiting the bulk of paper, and with previous Directives governing book manufacture.